AMERICAN GEOGRAPHICAL SOCIETY
SPECIAL PUBLICATION NO. 26
Edited by John C. Weaver

THE FACE OF
SOUTH AMERICA

An Aerial Traverse

By

JOHN LYON RICH
University of Cincinnati

AMERICAN GEOGRAPHICAL SOCIETY
NEW YORK
1942

George Grady Press, New York
Phoenix Engraving Company, New York

To the Memory of
THOMAS RICH
and
MARION LYON RICH
My Father and Mother

CONTENTS

INTRODUCTION

T HIS is primarily a book of pictures—not random snapshots, but air pictures deliberately made and selected to record as much as possible of the broader features of South America that unfold below the traveler in an ever changing but all too easily forgotten panorama along the skyway that nearly encircles the continent.

The air traveler has a perspective of a totally different order from that of the man on the ground. Wherever he looks, in each of a myriad of single views, he sees grouped in their mutual relations all the features of relief, geology, vegetation, and human occupance of hundreds or thousands of square miles of country. In a single flight over a region he can often obtain a clearer impression of the significant features of the terrain and of how it is being used by the people dwelling upon it than he could in months of exploration on the ground, and for the record all that are needed are a convenient camera and a technique by which the location of each picture can later be determined.[1]

Ever since air lines were first established around South America I had cherished the hope of one day seeing something of that continent from the air. The opportunity came in the first half of 1939 when sabbatical leave from the University of Cincinnati made such a journey possible. The apparent success of earlier experiments with the photographic aerial traverse[2]—the recording by means of accurately located photographs of the most characteristic and significant natural and cultural features along a line of flight—had encouraged an ambition to bring back a record from South America that would be of value to scientists in the fields of geography, geology, and ecology as well as to the layman interested in gaining a clearer impression of the natural background of South American development.

Since in 1939 most of the South American countries prohibited photography from the planes of the commercial air lines, fulfillment of that ambition was made possible only by special permission, here gratefully

---

[1] For the details of such a technique see John L. Rich: The Aerial Traverse—An Application of Aerial Photography to Geographic Studies, *Ohio Journ. of Sci.*, Vol. 41, 1941, pp. 212–224.

[2] John L. Rich: A Bird's-Eye Cross Section of the Central Appalachian Mountains and Plateau: Washington to Cincinnati, *Geogr. Rev.*, Vol. 29, 1939, pp. 561–586.

acknowledged, from the governments of Brazil, Uruguay, the Argentine Republic, Chile, Peru, Ecuador, and Colombia to photograph from the regular planes of Pan American Airways and its subsidiaries. For their good offices in helping to arrange for the permits I am greatly indebted to President Raymond Walters of the University of Cincinnati and to the American Geographical Society.

The route followed the east coast from Trinidad to Buenos Aires via Georgetown, Belém, Recife, Rio de Janeiro, São Paulo, Curitiba, and Asunción, thence across the Pampa and the Andes to Santiago, and back along the west coast to Panamá, with a side trip to Bogotá. Favored by generally good weather and visibility, we were able to see a strip of country 30 to more than 100 miles wide for almost the entire distance, except over French Guiana (obscured by clouds), and to bring back a photographic record of the significant features of most of that belt.

All photographs were taken with a miniature camera using 35-millimeter motion-picture film. It was necessary to photograph through the glass of the plane window, which, along the east coast, where flying boats were used, was always noticeably clouded by dried ocean spray. Fortunately, however, its effects are rarely noticeable. In the plane I carried copies of the sheets, photographically reduced to units of size convenient for my purpose, of the American Geographical Society's "Map of Hispanic America on the Scale of 1:1,000,000" for all of the route for which they were available, and the flight maps on pages 282–288 are based on these sheets. With the Society's maps in hand it was possible to record the time of passing recognizable landmarks and thereby subsequently to reconstruct the line of flight. Notation of the time when each picture was taken permitted later spotting of its position along that line. In numerous instances the positions of the camera stations along the flight line were checked by means of rough three-point resections on points imaged on the photographs which could be approximately identified on the map.[3]

In the caption of each photograph the location of the point over which it was calculated to have been taken is given to the nearest minute of

---

[3] O. M. Miller: Planetabling from the Air: An Approximate Method of Plotting from Oblique Aerial Photographs, *Geogr. Rev.*, Vol. 21, 1931, pp. 201–212; *idem:* Additional Notes on "Planetabling from the Air," *ibid.*, pp. 660–662.

latitude and longitude (a little more than a mile). Actually, the accuracy of these locations varies along the route. Where the terrain had been mapped with reasonable precision, there was generally little difficulty in recognizing a sufficient number of control points, and I believe most of the picture locations are correct within about 1 mile; but in the relatively unexplored areas where even the best maps are extremely sketchy, accurate control points were not available and consequently the locations given may be in error—in a few instances perhaps by as much as 10 miles.

The parts of the route concerning which there is most uncertainty are: along the flat lands near the mouth of the Amazon and farther east in northern Brazil, where the material available for the American Geographical Society's Millionth Map compilation is of recognizedly poor grade owing to the lack of original surveys; between Camocim and Recife, where clouds as well as the sparsity and indefinite nature of control points made exact location impossible; between the Río Tebicuary, south of Asunción, and Mercedes, in the northern part of the Argentine Republic, where less reliable map information and a storm may have introduced errors in the determination of the route as great as 5 to 10 miles east and west; and between Antioquia and the Río Atrato, in northwestern Colombia, where the calculated positions along the flight line did not check satisfactorily with available Colombian maps,[4] either because of extreme and unsuspected variations in wind velocity or because of inaccuracies in the maps.

In the accompanying text I have endeavored to explain briefly the salient features of each picture, to place it in its proper geographical setting, and to indicate its broader significance. The descriptions incorporate the results of a study of all the 966 pictures taken on the flight (fewer than one-third of which are here reproduced), as well as of fairly copious notes made at the time. Thus the descriptions contain considerably more information than could be deduced from the accompanying pictures alone. In addition, various facts gleaned from other sources have been included, but no attempt has been made to review the literature exhaustively.

Without the extremely valuable base provided by the American Geo-

---

[4] The American Geographical Society's Millionth Map sheet covering this section had not been compiled at the time the flight was made.

graphical Society's Map of Hispanic America, not only the reasonably accurate location of the pictures along the flight lines but also their description would have been much more difficult.

As all pictures were taken in the course of regularly scheduled flights, under whatever conditions of weather, haze, and lighting happened to prevail and at various heights up to nearly 15,000 feet (over northeastern Brazil), some of them are not as clear as might be desired. They have nevertheless been reproduced because they constitute a usable record of the terrain.

Many of the pictures include clouds and cloud shadows, which may prove confusing to the novice in the interpretation of air photographs. A few minutes' study of pictures such as several of those off the mouths of the Amazon, in which both clouds and their companion shadows are shown, should, however, quickly familiarize the reader with varied cloud effects and thus dispel any difficulty in this connection.

The scale of the pictures, which depends on the altitudes from which they were taken, may also be difficult to judge. Where trees are present, they are useful in suggesting relative scale, but in barren deserts such as those along the west coast, the problem is admitttedly difficult. There, roads or trails may give the desired clues.

The flight maps (pp. 282–288) show the line of flight and the position, direction, and approximate area covered by each picture. Major coast-line and drainage features and the principal towns have been included for easy identification of localities.

In books of travel and in the press, South America is repeatedly char-acterized by such expressions as "a land of opportunity" or "a land of untold riches." To one, however, who has made the circuit of the continent by air and has also spent considerable time on the ground outside the principal cities it would seem more aptly characterized as "a land of baffling unsolved problems." The riches are there—in places—and the opportunities likewise, but on the whole they are opportunities for improvement and development by large-scale coördinated and scien-tifically guided effort directed toward the well-being of the local society as a whole rather than opportunities for the individual pioneer settler such as abounded in North America a hundred and fifty years ago.

The problems are many and baffling: the use, other than for pasture, for the vast areas of tropical grassland and brushland, where a deluge of rain in one season is followed by long months of drought in the next; the development of tree crops suited to the tropical forest lands and the provision of markets for their products; the conquest of malaria in the valley lowlands; the development of, and possible uses for, the enormous potential water power along such streams as the Paraná and the southern tributaries of the Amazon; the almost total lack of coal and iron, and the limited water power of such a great country as the Argentine Republic; the inadequacies of land transportation; the large individual landholdings; and, finally, the extremely difficult problems created in the Andean regions by the fact that an overwhelming majority of the population is made up of Indians whose social and economic system was broken up at the time of the Spanish conquest, whose best lands were taken from them, and who ever since have been living in poverty and degradation, eking out a scanty subsistence from the less desirable sections of the steep, cold, and arid highlands, where whites in equal numbers would long ago have starved, even if they could have endured the rarefied air.

Many, though not all, of these problems are illustrated by the pictures or have been touched upon in the accompanying descriptions. Many of them do not present themselves with their full impact to the casual traveler who spends a few days or weeks in the principal cities, especially if he travels from one city to another by sea. The cities, like the flowers of a plant, depend on what is behind them for life and nourishment. They may be beautiful, and, as in the case of some capitals, they may be even more elaborate than the resources supporting them properly warrant, but they are, after all, nourished by the country surrounding them. It is this countryside that the air traveler is able to see to better advantage than others. He is, therefore, in a position to appreciate the problems and to formulate at least tentative judgments as to the ultimate possibilities of the various regions.

The pictures of the various parts of the continent reveal a wide variety of environments determined by relief and climate and suggest how these may have influenced settlement and development. For example, the lowland tropical rain forests stretching along the line of flight from the mouth of the Orinoco to São Luiz, as well as those of northwestern

Colombia and the Isthmus of Panamá, have, in general, successfully resisted all attempts at development. The pictures and the history of such regions show that those forests are unsuitable for the individual pioneer. However, the extensive plantations on the lowlands of the Guianas occupy former unforested swampy areas along the coasts.

The dry area of northeastern Brazil was colonized before the pilgrims landed at Plymouth Rock, but it still remains a "problem area." The higher parts, where the rainfall is more dependable, are rather densely settled, as the pictures show, but the successful development of most of that vast area has been held back by repeated devastating droughts. Whether an extensive government-sponsored system of reservoirs for flood storage and irrigation will solve the worst of the difficulties has not yet been fully demonstrated. Here, as elsewhere, the idea of a "land of opportunity" needs serious qualification. On the other hand, in a transition zone centering around São Luiz, between the rain forests to the west and the brushland or caatinga to the east, there seems to be a possible opportunity for the development of a highly important industry if the oil palm, or babassu, a tree native to this region, were to be cultivated in plantation style and the proper machinery were developed for the extraction of the oil.

Along the east coast, from Recife to Vitória, the pictures show only the coastal belt and, unfortunately, do not portray the more settled highlands farther inland, though the general character of these can be inferred in part from the photographs of the highlands northwest of Recife. Except for the sugar plantations between Recife and Maceió, the photographic record shows most of the east coast to be a sparsely settled, slightly dissected plain with sandy soils that seems to offer little promise for future development, except perhaps through the cultivation of coconuts, which evidently thrive. There seems to be no reason, except possibly a lack of cheap labor, why the region should not contribute largely to the coconut supply of the western hemisphere.

As the pictures clearly show, facilities for land transportation parallel to the coast are practically nonexistent. Inland, on the lower slopes of the upland and along some of the river valleys nearer the coast, is the seat of the world's second largest cacao-growing industry. Only a few of the cacao-shipping ports appear in our photographic record. From these, roads and railroads extend inland to the cacao plantations, but the ports are virtually isolated from one another except by sea.

Between Vitória and Rio de Janeiro, as is amply attested by the pictures, a combination of accessibility, altitude, and a marketable crop (coffee) has led to intensive mountain culture in spite of relatively dense tropical forests. In a similar environment between Rio de Janeiro and São Paulo, for some reason not evident in the topography, a coffee culture has not been established. Perhaps this is because the more accessible and more easily cultivated coffee lands northwest of São Paulo were more attractive to settlers.

Most of the region between São Paulo and Curitiba is an unbroken wilderness, the rough topography of which is likely to postpone development indefinitely. West of Curitiba, however, the cuesta lands offer favorable soils and climate. They have been rather fully developed in the eastern part, though they are still in the pioneer stage to the west where the lower valleys are plagued by malaria. For at least a hundred miles on each side of the Río Paraná the forests remain almost unbroken in spite of their accessibility by way of the river and of a gently rolling topography and volcanic soil that, in a region with a more favorable climate and freedom from malaria, would certainly have invited settlement.

The part of eastern Paraguay along our route is covered by a practically uninterrupted forest. In the central part, and westward to the lowlands of the Río Paraguay, the country supports a relatively dense population, but farther south the river lowlands, because of the frequency of flooding, are probably permanently in pasture.

In the Argentine Republic, Corrientes Province and the northern part of Entre Ríos Province evidently are still in the pioneer stage of development. The intensive cultivation of the Río Paraná delta shows what can be done with a fertile alluvial soil where a near-by market exerts its full stimulating effect. Between Buenos Aires and Córdoba the best parts of the Pampa are portrayed — fully developed except for the fact that many large landholdings seem here and there to have perpetuated a pastoral economy which would otherwise have given way to the prevailing culture of grain. West of Córdoba we enter the semiarid belt, where, aside from the restricted areas along the base of the Andes where mountain streams permit irrigation, only a limited pastoral economy is possible.

In the fruit-growing region around Mendoza, available water for irrigation seems already to have been fully utilized.

On the west coast, both in Chile (north of Santiago) and in Peru, life is dominated by the aridity of the climate. Agricultural activity is closely confined to the relatively few valleys where water from the mountains is available for irrigation, and even mining, in a region where mineral deposits are rich and widely distributed, is seriously handicapped by lack of water. Of the social problems generated by the concentration of ownership of the irrigable land in comparatively few hands, this is not the place for an extended discussion. However, offsetting some of the social disadvantages of large landholdings is the fact that intensive plantation culture on a large scale, such as that of sugar and cotton on the great haciendas, would scarcely be possible otherwise, and it may well be questioned whether as many people would gain as good a living from the same ground if it were subdivided into small private ownerships.

Our air route over the deserts near the coast did not give opportunity to portray the difficult conditions under which the predominantly Indian population of the Andean highlands is gaining a meager livelihood under adverse circumstances. Nevertheless, several weeks on the ground in the highlands showed that the social problems there are perhaps even more pressing than in the coastal valleys.

The pictorial record will serve, however, to show that these west-coast countries are not the rich, undeveloped promised land that one might suppose from much of the current literature. In the lowland valleys, a well as on the highlands, possible agricultural land has on the whole been much more fully utilized and supports a denser population than in North America.

In the northern countries—Ecuador and Colombia—the greater rainfall on the highlands and the tropical heat of the lowlands have led to a concentration of the population on the higher lands, under generally much more favorable natural conditions than in the countries farther south. Here, also, most of the tillable land has been occupied, and much of it, under pressure of population, is being cultivated in the presence of topographic handicaps that would seem prohibitive to farmers of the United States or Canada.

Considering the route as a whole, it is worthy of note that only comparatively small parts of the areas crossed were found to be free of
serious handicaps of topography or climate or both. It is true that some
of the most favorable regions, such as the uplands of Brazil northwest of
São Paulo, were off the route and consequently are not represented, but
it must be borne in mind that much of South America, where grassy
plains seem to invite the settler, is in the tropical belt, in which ordinary
agriculture cannot yet be successfully practiced.

In general, South America was peopled by Europeans at a considerably earlier date than North America. That it has not been peopled and
developed so completely or so rapidly becomes more and more under-
standable as climatic and topographic disadvantages are better known
and appreciated. In the favorable areas, the density of population and
the intensiveness of cultivation are in many cases surprising. In Brazil,
particularly, great resources of water power still remain undeveloped,
but they promise in the future to make up, to a considerable degree,
for inadequate and rather inconveniently located coal resources. The
scarcity of coal in South America has one result fully appreciated by
the air traveler—the almost complete absence of smoke. To one return-
ing to the United States after several months in smoke-free air, the black
pall that hangs over much of his native land comes as a distinct shock.

If South America is a "land of opportunity," study of the pictures
and of their accompanying descriptions will, I think, suggest that,
although much of the continent has opportunities for great further
development, those opportunities, more often than not, will be realized
only through the intelligent application of scientific knowledge to the
conquest of adverse conditions.

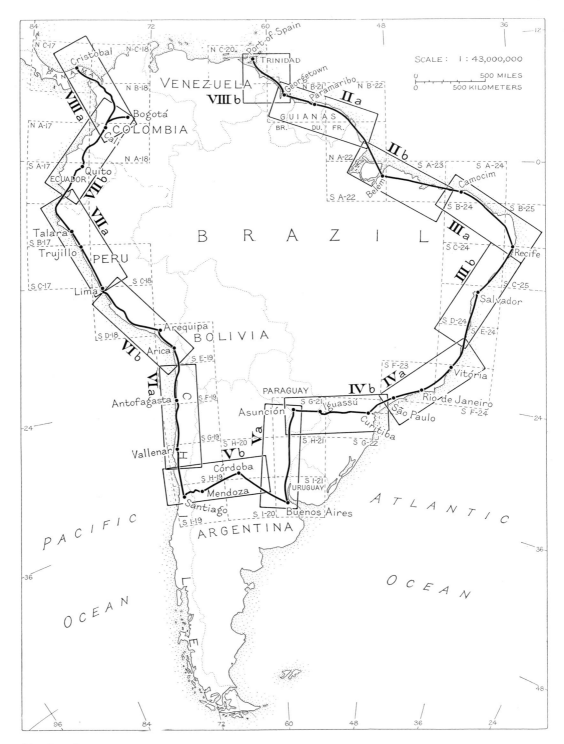

MAP I. The line of flight around South America. The sections of the route enclosed by solid lines and designated by Roman numerals and small letters are shown in detail in Maps II to VIII, pp. 282–288. The sheets of the American Geographical Society's Map of Hispanic America, 1:1,000,000, used in the plotting of the flight course and the preparation of the sectional maps are indicated by dotted lines and serial numbers.

THE GUIANAS*

Aᶠᵗᵉʳ a dawn take-off from Port-of-Spain, Trinidad, our Pan American Airways "Brazilian Clipper" crossed about midway of the southern shore of Trinidad at 6.18 heading on a course about S. 27°E. toward the mouths of the Orinoco River. Six minutes later the flat coast of Venezuela could be dimly seen far to the right, and about 25 miles out from Trinidad a distinct line, trending nearly northeast-southwest, marked the junction of the deep blue water, over which we had been flying, with the muddy water that we were to find off the mouths and over the delta of the Orinoco and at intervals all along the coasts of British and Dutch Guiana and of northern Brazil. At first, the muddy water had a light greenish color, which changed within 5 or 6 miles to a "coffee and cream" yellowish brown. We passed about 10 miles offshore from Punta Baja, then changed course to about S. 56°E. This carried us out of sight of land opposite the main mouths of the Orinoco, but gave opportunity to determine the approximate boundaries of the sediment-laden water. The results indicated on the sketch map (Map VIIIb, p. 288, below) are of interest in showing the pronounced effect of the littoral current in carrying the Orinoco mud northward along the coast.

British Guiana

Land was sighted again from about 10 miles off the large estuarine mouth of the Waini River near the western border of British Guiana. From here to the mouth of the Pomeroon River the coast is low and sandy, with sand bars tying to the shore in such a way as to indicate a littoral current from the southeast.

The coast is completely forested west of about longitude 59°7′, east of which it is bordered as far as the Pomeroon River by grassy swampland or savanna. The grassy belt, locally separated from the shore by a narrow strip of forest, widens eastward to 10 miles or more near the Pomeroon River. Behind it is forest, everywhere unbroken except for occasional lakes of considerable size. No evidences of human occupation were noted before reaching the Pomeroon River.

The water of the rivers has a deep brown color caused by organic

---

* See Map II, p. 282, below.

materials derived from the swamps and forests. This "black water" can be seen in the ocean for a quarter of a mile or more along shore opposite the smaller streams, and extends out from the mouth of the Pomeroon River for at least a mile. "Black water" is characteristic of most of the rivers of the Guianas except the larger ones, which are muddy, and the smaller ones after heavy rains. The total amount of organic matter thus carried to the sea in solution must be very great. If precipitated, such material must be an important source of the organic content of the offshore sediments. It seems worthy of consideration as a possible origin of source material for oil.

As a probable effect of the strong northwestward drift of the sediment along the coast, nearly all the streams of the Guianas are deflected for many miles in that direction before entering the ocean.[1] In typical fashion, the Pomeroon River comes down from the interior to within about 3 miles of the coast, then turns at right angles and flows northwestward for about 18 miles before emptying into the sea.

Along the lower few miles of the river the first cultivated land appeared, extending back for a mile or more on either side of the stream, but not continuously [1].[2] The crop appeared to be mainly bananas, and there was a strong suggestion that the jungle is encroaching on former more extensive cultivation. On the far (southwest) side of the river, beyond the clearings on the natural levee, all is forest for a distance of 5 to 10 miles, beyond which a belt of lakes or marshy grasslands a few miles wide may be seen extending roughly parallel to the river. In the foreground between the natural levee in the immediate vicinity of the river and the coast is brushy savanna. Two or three miles offshore a continuous belt of whitecaps testifies to the gently shelving nature of the sea bottom.

A narrow strip of cultivated land, or, probably more exactly, land formerly cultivated, follows the river to its bend and for several miles upstream. On either side the forest is unbroken. Here, as elsewhere in the Guianas away from the coast, the rivers, by furnishing a means of transport, have localized settlement close to their banks. A natural levee of higher ground close to the river may also have controlled settlement in this case.

---

[1] See Map II, p. 282, below.
[2] Figures in square brackets refer to photographs.

About 4 miles beyond the bend of the Pomeroon River, old fence lines and partly overgrown fields [2] indicate abandoned attempts to cultivate the border zone between the coastal savanna and the forest. This region, as well as the banks of the Pomeroon River, apparently represented the extreme westward pioneer fringe of plantation culture in the period of its greatest extension. This was before the freeing of the slaves in 1838 brought about labor difficulties that made the operation of the more distant plantations unprofitable.

Close inspection of the photograph reveals not only the abandoned plantations, together with a possibly active one at the upper left, but also the mixed savanna and forest character of the vegetation of the uncleared land—a characteristic condition close to the coast in this section.

The transition from the partly abandoned pioneer fringe to the heart of the rich plantation land of western British Guiana is abrupt, for within 5 miles (about 40 miles northwest of Georgetown) we are over intensively cultivated plantations mainly of sugar and rice, though coconuts and perhaps cacao are also grown [3, 4, 5].

The general arrangement of the plantations is clearly shown in Figure 3. Canals, marked by the more prominent lines of trees, extend back from the coast at about a quarter of a mile intervals. They furnish the only means of transportation for the crops, and are also used for drainage or irrigation as occasion may require. Toward the back (right, top) of the cultivated area many of the fields appear to be fallow. The plantation area is separated from the uncultivated land behind it by a dike which protects the drained land against inundation from farther inland. Beyond the dike, visible near the top of the picture, are temporary lakes and grassy savannas grading into the jungle which extends inland beyond the bounds of vision. The savannas are utilized for pasture, while the lakes serve as storage reservoirs for water occasionally needed for irrigation.

Rice paddies form an interesting pattern in the more detailed view of the plantations afforded by Figure 4. At the upper right sugar cane can be recognized. In both this and the preceding picture it is noteworthy that only one group of buildings is to be seen. The people live almost exclusively in a narrow belt close to the coast, as in Figure 5, showing a coastal village, probably Daniels-town, and numerous dwellings strung out along the coastal highway. Characteristic features are the broad belt

1. A view across the Pomeroon River, showing the westernmost position of crop cultivation in British Guiana (SW, from 7°34′ N., 58°40′ W.)
    (On the titles to the photographs approximate directions and positions are indicated in parentheses)

2. Abandoned clearings east of the Pomeroon River (SW, from 7°22′ N., 58°32′ W.)

3. Plantations in western British Guiana, about 44 miles northwest of Georgetown (SW, from 7° 19′ N., 58° 30′ W.). Looking inland from a position near the coast

4. A more detailed view of plantations and canals about 43 miles northwest of Georgetown (from 7° 18′ N., 58° 30′ W.)

5. Typical culture patterns along the coast of western British Guiana, 40 miles northwest of Georgetown (S, from 7°17′ N., 58°29′ W.)

6. Sugar plantations 5 miles west of Georgetown (SW, from 6°50′ N., 58°14′ W.)

of mud flats exposed at low tide between the water (marked by ocean swells) and the line of vegetation along the shore; the narrow belt of un-reclaimed wet savanna and brush close to the shore; the sea wall, visible a short distance back from the shore at the right, with its sluice gate or lock controlling the water in the canal system where the river crosses the sea wall near the center of the picture; the highway close to the coast, connecting the villages and localizing settlement; the group of large buildings, presumably warehouses or processing sheds, to the left of the village, with a wide moat in front of them; the sugar mill at the upper right; and the plantations which support the whole.

These three pictures epitomize the economy of the entire plantation belt of British Guiana and, taken in reverse order, reveal a complete cross section from the coast to the inland jungle: the low, muddy coast, the sea wall, the narrow belt of settlement, the plantations, the inland dike, the lakes and savannas, and finally the unbroken forest. British Guiana from the air is especially beautiful—rich, black soil visible in the rice paddies, neat dwellings and well kept fields, the brilliant green of the sugar plan-tations, the light but less brilliant green of the savannas, and the somber green of the jungle together paint a picture such as only the air traveler is privileged to see, and even he rarely.

Leaving the coast, we take a direct course across the wide, drowned mouth of the Essequibo River toward Georgetown. Though the delta of the Essequibo does not appear above the water, its outline is clearly dis-cernible below the sea surface, as is shown by a photograph [7] looking northeasterly across the northwest side of the delta. No part of the delta in the area covered by this photograph appears to rise above sea level, although in several places the water is shallow enough to cause the waves to break. The lobate delta form can be clearly seen.

After crossing the Essequibo estuary, we flew over the coast about 8 miles west of Georgetown. Here the cultivated plain extends back for several miles. Towns are strung out along a jetty-protected coast. Planta-tion culture is mainly sugar cane. Figure 6 shows one of the larger sugar plantations with its canals. Light and shadow under the cumulus clouds is striking indeed in Guiana, but in a photograph is likely to be confusing, as in this picture, where the foreground in shadow contrasts in an unreal fashion with the sunlit area in the distance.

For about 20 miles east of Georgetown we flew close to the coast over continuous plantations of the type already described, but with cacao and coconuts more prominent. Habitation is confined entirely to a narrow strip along the coast, which is followed by a railroad and a highway. The plantations extend back 5 to 8 or more miles, and beyond this is jungle. Communication back of the immediate coastal strip is entirely by canals.

The typical pattern of this region is well illustrated in the photograph taken near Clonbrook [9], about 16 miles southeast of Georgetown. Cultural features are similar to those shown in Figure 5 west of Georgetown, except for the extensive coconut or cacao groves appearing in the background. Jetties protect the sea front, and a dredged channel, leading through a sluice gate in the sea wall at the left, connects with the canal system leading to the town and the plantations. On the right the picture covers part of, or is at least very close to, the Plantation Hope.[3]

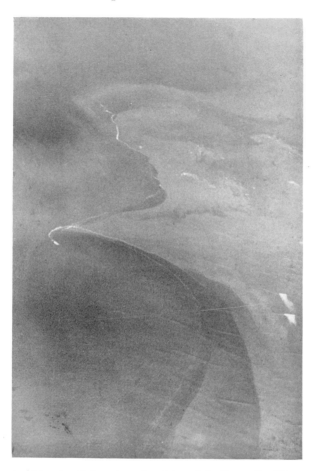

7. Margin of the submarine delta of the Essequibo River (NE, from 7° 11′ N., 58° 26′ W.)

After following the coast for about 20 miles southeast of Georgetown,

[3] Robert S. Platt: Reconnaissance in British Guiana, with Comments on Microgeography, *Annals Assn. of Amer. Geogrs.*, Vol. 29, 1939, pp. 105–126.

our route passed out to sea on a straight line for Paramaribo. Interesting patterns formed by the mixing of muddy river water with the blue sea water were noted 8 miles from the nearest shore, about 20 miles from the mouth of the Berbice River. Enormous cumulus clouds were skirted at intervals [8], or gave a few moments of rough air as we passed through their tops.

Dutch Guiana

Approaching land again in Dutch Guiana, we pass offshore from the mouths of the Coppename and Saramacca rivers [10]. Like other streams of the Guianas these mouth in broad estuaries which they seem to be filling rapidly. Wide mud flats appear at low tide, backed by extensive grassy savanna, grading inland into low brush.

Fifteen miles farther

8.   Skirting tall cumulus clouds off the coast of British Guiana (S, from 6°39' N., 57°42' W.)

east, Figure 11, looking south-southwest from about 2 miles inland, shows the essential features of this region. A grassy savanna with scattered low brush extends from the coast to the Saramacca River in the background. It is uncultivated except for a narrow belt close to the river, presumably on the natural levee. Beyond the river is a strip of grassland 2 or 3 miles wide, giving way to forest farther back.

As we approach Paramaribo, the first cultivated land appears 9 or 10 miles west of the city, but, as shown in the photograph [12], the cultivation is much less intensive than in British Guiana, and the pattern of settlement is different. Scattered houses are located at more or less regular intervals along the canals as if cultivation were being done by private owners living on the land. These undoubtedly are part of the holdings of the Dutch colonists who settled near Paramaribo in 1845.[4] In this view we are looking southward across the canal that connects Paramaribo with the Saramacca River. The canal passes from left to right across the middle of the picture, and then, as the picture shows, follows the winding and probably canalized course of Wanica Kreek southward to the Saramacca River. This canal is one unit in a system of inland waterways by which it is possible to travel entirely across Dutch Guiana, following the low belt behind the broad coastal bars that have deflected many of the Guiana rivers northwestward before they enter the sea.

In Paramaribo, several large lumber mills were receiving their logs from the Suriname River. At the airport, during a refueling stop, passengers were reminded of one of the most important products of the colony by being served delicious hot chocolate. That it was a Dutch colony was amply attested by the spotless cleanliness of everything about the premises.

Eastward from Paramaribo, the first 7 or 8 miles of the peninsula between the Suriname and Commewijne rivers was found to be intensively cultivated in plantation style with sugar and rice predominating, but with much coffee and cacao grown beneath stately shading trees planted in rows as in Figure 13. Figure 14, looking southward from about 8 miles east of Paramaribo, shows a typical plantation. Only a short distance back, at the margin of the plantation is unbroken jungle. In the background of both this picture and of Figure 13 is the Suriname River.

A more comprehensive view of the plantations east of Paramaribo is afforded by Figure 15, looking northwestward over the peninsula between the Commewijne and Suriname rivers and the wide estuary of the two. This peninsula, all within 12 miles of Paramaribo, was the only part of Dutch Guiana where large-scale plantation culture was noted. Elsewhere cultivation seemed to be in small units, presumably controlled by individual owners. In this respect Dutch Guiana contrasts strongly with neighboring British Guiana.

---

[4] See W. Van Royen: White Colonization in Dutch Guiana, *Geogr. Rev.*, Vol. 29, 1939, pp. 330–331.

As we fly eastward from Paramaribo it is only 15 miles before the edge of the jungle is reached. Figure 16, looking southward, shows the transition within a distance of a little over a mile from considerable culture to unbroken jungle.

Farther east, culture is restricted to belts a mile, more or less, in width bordering the rivers, as shown in Figure 17, looking north-northeast from a point 25 miles S. 82°E. from Paramaribo. In the foreground is the Boven Commewijne River and in the background the Commewijne River. Houses may be recognized along the river bank, but no roads appear. About 3 miles farther on (upstream on the Boven Commewijne River) the limit of cultivation is obviously close at hand [18]. Only small clearings appear, and in the woods in the left background the outlines of former fields, now overgrown, testify either to a losing fight against the jungle or to the primitive "shifting culture" which is commonly practiced by the natives. The rectilinear pattern of overgrown fields, as compared with the irregular pattern of the more recent clearings, suggests the abandonment of former European holdings.

About 41 miles S. 84°E. from Paramaribo, in unbroken jungle, a pronounced alignment of the forest was noted extending approximately east and west, or a little north of east. The alignment occurs along a belt a mile or two wide, terminating sharply on its southern side [19]. It is interpreted as a series of beach ridges formed at a time of former lower land level. The beaches are about 15 miles inland from the present coast, and seemingly record a certain amount of uplift of the land. However, they are not as high as might be judged from their distance from the coast, for a low belt intervenes that makes it possible to go by boat from Paramaribo to the Marowijne River by way of the Cottica River and Wane Kreek. The photograph is particularly interesting in showing that even in virgin jungle, landscape features of low relief may be visible from the air, particularly if they involve variations in the underlying rock or soil which may be reflected in the vegetation.

The juxtaposition of evidences of relative land subsidence provided by the estuaries of the rivers and of emergence indicated by the raised beaches is noteworthy, particularly as a similar condition was observed at various places along the eastern coast, especially north of Vitória, Brazil, and near Buenos Aires.

From the site of the raised beaches eastward to the border of French

Guiana some of the ground was obscured by clouds, but all that was seen was jungle with a few small patches of clearing scattered at random.

Since French Guiana was almost entirely covered by clouds, we saw nothing of that country except for occasional glimpses through holes in the clouds that revealed unbroken jungle everywhere. At 12,000 to nearly 15,000 feet we were above all but a few of the taller cumulus clouds that rose here and there above the billowy but generally even top of the overcast.

British and Dutch Guiana together constitute a most interesting example of what can be done in a wet tropical lowland, and also of the influence of experience in conquering particular environments.[5] To the traveler visiting British Guiana for the first time it comes as a surprise to find a system of canals and polders like those of Holland, but when he realizes that the entire area was once colonized by the Dutch, the surprise is lessened. Guiana, with its flat, wet, alluvial coast is admirably suited to the type of cultivation the Dutch had learned at home. The prevalence of houses supported on posts is easily explained by the flatness and wetness of the land. Why roofs should be made almost exclusively of galvanized iron is not so clear.

Comparison of the generally neat and well kept appearance of the large-scale commercial plantations both in British Guiana and on the peninsula east of Paramaribo, with the land under individual ownership in both colonies, emphasizes the well known fact that the small landowner cannot, as a rule, successfully combat the jungle and the other disadvantages of the wet tropics.

---

[5] See R. R. Platt and others: The European Possessions in the Caribbean Area . . ., *Amer. Geogr. Soc., Map of Hispanic America Publ. No. 4*, New York, 1941, pp. 40–45, 79–85, 102–105.

9. The cultivated coastal zone 16 miles east-southeast of Georgetown (S, from 6°44′ N., 57°57′ W.)

10. The estuarine mouth of the Coppename and Saramacca rivers (SSW, from 5°59′ N., 55°53′ W.). Grass-covered flats in the middle distance

11. Savanna and low brush between the coast and the Saramacca River (SSW, from 5°56′ N., 55°41′ W.). Levee culture along river

12. Characteristic culture patterns about 8 miles west of Paramaribo (S, from 5°51′ N., 55°20′ W.)

13. Plantation culture under shading trees—cacao or coffee—6 miles east of Paramaribo (SW, from 5°50′ N., 55°7′ W.). The Suriname River in the background

14. Plantation agriculture in Dutch Guiana, 8 miles east of Paramaribo (SSW, from 5°50′ N., 55°6′ W.). The crop shown here is probably sugar. Typical jungle in background

15. Cacao, sugar, and rice plantations on the peninsula between the Suriname and Commewijne rivers, 10 miles east of Paramaribo (NW, from 5°49′ N., 55°4′ W.)

16. The "pioneer fringe." Transition from plantation agriculture to unbroken jungle, 15 miles east-southeast of Paramaribo (S, from 5°48′ N., 55°0′ W.)

17. Croplands along the Boven Commewijne River (NNE, from 5°45′ N., 54°51′ W.)

18. Abandoned clearings or possibly a desultory shifting culture along the riverbanks (NE, from 5°44′ N., 54°47′ W.)

19. Striking vegetation patterns reveal the presence of abandoned sea beaches in the jungle about 15 miles inland (ENE, from 5°42′ N., 54°37′ W.)

20. North end of Ilha de Maracá and the tidal inlet of Igarapé do Inferno (WSW, from 2°16′ N., 50°5′ W.). In the foreground are the streaked patterns produced by muddy water mixing with clear

BRAZIL: MOUTHS OF THE AMAZON TO RECIFE*

Mouths of the Amazon

AFTER two hours above the clouds over French Guiana, our first glimpse of Brazil was of swampland near the Rio Uacá at about 3°41′ N., 51°26′ W. Twenty-two minutes later we crossed the coast line at about 3°N., and continued out to sea to a point 15 miles east of Cabo do Norte on Maracá Island [20], where the course was changed to S. 23°E. toward Belém (Pará).

Off the north end of Maracá we encountered the red muddy water of the Amazon streaking northeastward and mingling with the clear blue ocean water. The nature of the contact is well shown in the foreground of Figure 20, where the lighter streaks slanting down toward the right indicate the muddy water. Some of the sharp-pointed muddy streaks extended forward for 2 or more miles. Similar streaking at the margin of muddy water had already been noted off the Orinoco as well as some of the Guiana rivers, but in other places the mixing produced an irregular blotchy pattern.

The north end of the low island of Maracá, with the broad tidal inlet of Igarapé do Inferno, lies about 15 miles to the west. On its eastern side, in the left third of the picture, is a vague indication of an old shore line such as appears farther south.

Passing Cabo Raso within a few miles of the coast [21], we have an opportunity to observe its details. The land is flat and swampy, with water showing through the trees in places, as in the light area at the lower right, and the mottled area near the upper left. It is crossed by large tidal inlets. A thicket of mangrove here comes to the water's edge and appears to cover almost the entire picture.

Mangrove, a shrubby tree adapted to growth in salt and brackish shallow water, is common along low tropical coasts. The tree is supported on numerous branching roots that take off from the trunk above water level and form an intricately entwined, impassable network that is very effective in holding sediment and permitting the encroachment of land upon the sea along shallow coasts.

---

* See Maps II and III, pp. 282 and 283, below.

Only a short distance beyond Cabo Raso there is evidence of what appears to be active prograding of the coast line [22]. At the right the waves are breaking against the mangrove thicket, but toward the left a wide bare mud flat is exposed at low tide. Farther back is one distinct old shore line, with another less distinct between it and the coast. Beyond the old shore line the jungle trees are much larger, and open water may be seen among them. Still farther back are small rivers meandering through the jungle.

A similar sequence of coastal features was observed southward to the Rio Araguarí estuary [23]. Looking forward, about S. 45°W. along the coast, one sees at the right the continuation of the features previously described, swinging round to the west and up the broad mouth of the Rio Araguarí, which appears under the wingbrace of the plane. To the right of the river's mouth are considerable areas of grassland, recognizable in the picture by their lighter shade as compared with the mangrove thickets that finger inland from the coast.

About 11 miles farther on, a view up the Rio Araguarí [24] reveals extensive silting along the south side of the main underwater channel. This is shown by the group of shoals at the left of the center and by the mud streaking of the water between the shoals and the center foreground. The thickets of mangrove at the right, backed by grassland, also appear in the preceding picture [23]. Scale can be judged by the fact that the center of the picture is calculated to be about 10 miles away. The plane was at approximately 10,000 feet.

Visible just behind the pontoon in Figure 25, is the broad estuarine mouth of Canal do Norte, one of the four principal distributaries of the Amazon. The powerful movement of sediment-laden water is clearly indicated by the streaky flow patterns.

In Figure 26 we are looking about S. 68°W. over the shoals that mark the north side of the underwater channel of Canal Perigoso north of Mexiana Island. (These shoals do not appear on the American Geographical Society map.[1]) The center of the picture is 11 miles away and the mainland behind the pontoon about 26 miles. Interesting flow patterns that connect the center foreground with the islands behind are revealed

---

[1] Map of Hispanic America on the Scale of 1:1,000,000; Sheet North A-22, Amapá. See also title to Map II, p. 282, below.

in the water over and around the shoals and mud flats. The dark flow streaks at the right present a puzzle. Farther south, beyond Salvador, somewhat similar patterns were made by floating algae of carrot-yellow color, but they photographed light [56]. Perhaps these dark streaks may be algae of another variety.

In the background of this picture, as well as in Figures 23, 24, and 25, are the interesting tall cumulus clouds that seem to be characteristic of the equatorial belt of Brazil. They rise as slender spires for thousands of feet above a low narrow base. Several have grown large enough to produce rain squalls, but the largest shower, in the background of Figure 26, is descending from a higher cloud.

It is difficult to imagine anything more interesting and more beautiful than an early afternoon offshore flight across the mouths of the Amazon. From the cool comfort of 10,000 feet in the air one enjoys a two-hour panorama of exquisite cloud formations, varied shades of green in jungle and grassland, and of infinitely diverse and fascinating patterns in color and form as the red waters of the Amazon mingle with the blue of the ocean.

The island of Mexiana is flat like the islands farther north, and is bordered along its eastern margin by a fringe of mangrove up to several miles wide. The central part of the island is grassland.

The eastern part of the island of Marajó, where crossed on a line extending from a point 10 miles east of the island of Mexiana to Belém, is almost entirely low, swampy grassland. Its northern shore [27] is bordered by a fringe of mangrove, which, while locally several miles wide (as in the foreground), is elsewhere very narrow (as in the background). Interesting details of the pattern and underwater features of tidal channels and coastal mud flats are revealed.

Across the northern 8 or 10 miles of Marajó [28], belts of successive additions to the island as it was built up by the muds brought down by the Amazon are clearly shown. The fringe of mangrove along the north coast appears under the clouds at the upper right, in addition to inland extensions along some of the drainage courses.

Farther inland the patterns formed by enlargement of the island gradually disappear and give place to vague patterns of former tidal channels, perhaps still occupied by water during the rainy season. Still farther

21. Cabo Raso, the easternmost point in South America north of the Amazon (WSW, from 1°43′ N., 49°52′ W.)

22. Coastal features south of Cabo Raso (SSW, from 1°41′ N., 49°51′ W.)

23. Mud flats, mangrove thickets, and old shore lines, at the mouth of the Rio Araguarí (SW, from 1°30′ N., 49°47′ W.)

24. A view up the Rio Araguarí (WSW, from 1°20′ N., 49°43′ W.). Shoals and typical cloud formations

25. Canal do Norte, one of the major distributaries of the Amazon (WSW, from 0°57′ N., 49°35′ W.). Note the patterns in the muddy water in the foreground

26. Current patterns and unmapped shoals in the muddy waters off the mouth of Canal Perigoso, one of the four principal distributary channels of the Amazon (WSW, from 0°25′ N., 49°22′ W.)

27. Mangrove thickets and tidal inlets along the northern shore of Ilha Marajó (W, from 0° 10′ S., 49° 7′ W.)

28. Old strand lines indicating successive additions to the land of northern Ilha Marajó (W, from 0°14′ S., 49°4′ W.)

29. Poorly organized drainage near the center of Ilha Marajó (W, from 0°37′ S., 48°55′ W.)

inland, near the center of the island along the route indicated, and according to the map, along the low drainage divide, Figure 29, taken from a height of 6000 to 8000 feet, shows a smooth, grassy plain on which partially interconnecting streams wander. Some of these show an alignment suggestive of shore features formed during the growth of the island. Somewhat indistinct streaks suggest cattle trails, although no definite indications of human habitation were noted anywhere along the Amazon mouths north of the southern few miles of Marajó Island. However, the island does support extensive herds of cattle.[2]

At point *A* on the route map [II], a position about 1°2′ N., 48°44′ W., it was noted that the island was decidedly swampy, but less so than farther north. About half of the surface appeared to be fairly dry. Rounded clumps of vegetation were noted, and a few habitations in small circular clearings. No extensive cultivation was seen. As we approached within about 2 miles of the Amazon, a fringe of forest appeared.

In a few minutes, the plane was over the moss-grown red tile roofs of Belém, an exotic river port surrounded by jungle to the very edges of the city, except for a small area devoted to market gardening.

In the late afternoon at Belém the daily shower had just passed, and the air was moist, though not uncomfortably hot. About the city the extensive use of tile is outstanding—as facing for buildings, as sidewalk paving, and forming the copy of advertising billboard displays. No doubt this is due to the deterioration of wood and paper in such a climate.

Belém to Camocim

After a dawn take-off from Belém we turned eastward, following the south side of the Rio Guamá. Twelve miles east of Belém the land along the river is forested, with small rounded clearings in all stages of reversion to forest—a typical "shifting culture" such as that pictured in Figures 33 and 34. The Rio Guamá, crossed at the big bend at longitude 48°W., was wine-colored from the mixture of a small amount of silt with the "black water" of the forests. For the next 140 miles clouds obscured the ground except for occasional glimpses of uninterrupted jungle in the

---

[2] For recent descriptions of the island and its industries see Hugh B. Cott: Wonder Island of the Amazon Delta, *Natl. Geogr. Mag.,* Vol. 74, 1938, pp. 635–670; and Desmond Holdridge: Feudal Island, New York, 1939.

last 80 miles of that distance. Ten miles farther on, the clouds had broken enough to permit the taking of a photograph [30], looking northward over a landscape of very uniform vegetation, and of flat or gently rolling topography.

The picture shows a type of low broken clouds, that over large areas had a pattern closely resembling a mackerel sky. These lay only a few hundred feet above the jungle most of the way from Belém. Presumably they represent an early morning condensation of moisture from the jungles. Their shapes reveal a wind from the east or northeast.

After another 35 miles of jungle we came out over swampland and savanna with brush hammocks, 5 miles west of the Rio Turiassú. A view northward to the coast [31] shows the river bordered by mangrove thickets, flowing through a savanna region with scattered rounded hammocks of forest. The existing details of the river mouth are in reality quite different from their portrayal on the maps.[3]

Looking upstream, about S. 40°W., from a mile and a half further on [32], one sees the stream bordered by a thicket, meandering on a grassy plain with jungle on either side. In the background are many large lakes (white in the picture) bordering the stream in a fashion suggesting that the main stream is aggrading and ponding its tributaries.

Looking steeply down northward as we cross the Rio Turiassú [33], we see all three of the vegetation associations (areas) typical of the region—the mangrove thickets along the river and bordering some of the oxbow lakes on the flood plain; the savanna on the flood plain; and beyond that the forest on a low, knobby, old-age erosion surface having an expression typical of crystalline rocks such as underlie this area. Here, as in the preceding picture, alluviation is indicated by the "drowned" condition of the upland border with respect to the river flats as seen at the left, and by the numerous outlying knobs rising above the flats.

Patterns of present and past clearings in the forest indicate habitation, and small houses were noted. However, such features are confined to a belt close to the river. Ten miles east of the river the topography was like that to the west, with a low, old-age hill land of small relief, covered by unbroken jungle.

Eighteen or 20 miles beyond the river we enter the western border of

---

[3] See title to Map II, p. 282, below.

an inhabited area tributary to São Luiz. Looking southward [34], we see a forested, late mature to old-age region of low relief, with abundant evidences of human occupation. New deadenings are scattered at rather wide intervals, and between them are old clearings in all stages of regrowth. This is a typical example of the shifting agriculture commonly practiced by the natives of the tropical forests, where the soil becomes depleted after a few years of cultivation and the fields are abandoned in favor of new clearings.

This and the preceding four pictures illustrate clearly the characteristic topographic, vegetational, and human patterns in the northwestern part of the state of Maranhão: the transition from mangrove thickets along the coast and rivers, inland through a narrow savanna belt to the forest; the primitive culture, mainly near the rivers; and the almost entire absence of any impression made by European culture upon the landscape.[4]

As we approach Baía de São Marcos [35], the forest gives way to a peculiar brushy savanna, apparently composed of tall grasses which are cleared for cultivation by the same shifting system that is practiced in the forest. Outlines of clearings can be recognized in the foreground, and comparison with the mangrove thickets along the river shows that these clearings cannot be in forest. The population here is fairly dense, although no roads or even recognizable trails appear on this or any of the preceding pictures. We are looking south, or a little east of south. The large tidal estuary in the background does not appear on any of the maps to which the writer has access. It is probably Baía de Cuman, and if so has been incorrectly represented on the maps.[5]

About 10 miles farther on [36], we come out over the estuary shown in the preceding picture, at the point where it is joined by a smaller stream, apparently that appearing in the lower left of Figure 35. Interesting underwater patterns can be seen, but the features of special interest are the numerous fish traps on the shoal opposite the mouth of the stream, all so placed as to catch the fish as they go out with the ebbing tide.

---

[4] For a recent excellent geographic treatment of this region, and a discussion of the placer gold mining that a few years ago brought in a considerable transient population, following the pacification of troublesome groups of Indians, see S. Fróis Abreu: Observações sôbre a Guiana Maranhense, *Rev. Brasileira de Geogr.*, Vol. 1, No. 4, 1939, pp. 26–54, including a summary in six languages. (Noted in *Geogr. Rev.*, Vol. 30, 1940, pp. 491–493.)

[5] See title to Map II, p. 282, below.

After crossing the estuary, we pass out over Baía de São Marcos near Ponta Itacolomí. A view south along the coast [37] reveals sea cliffs 150 feet or more high in the right foreground cut in bright red, apparently rather soft rocks. Cliff cutting has not yet straightened the coast enough to obscure the generally drowned nature of the region evidenced by the bays in the middle and in the background.

Eight miles farther out in the bay interesting patterns were noted, made by the mixing of muddy and clear water. Locally, red muddy water was distributed in flecks like those of cirrus clouds.

The eastern side of the Baía de São José estuary, the broad mouth of the Rio Itapecurú, is a maze of shoals, low mangrove-covered islands, and tidal inlets well illustrated in Figure 38. Over the whole area the water is so shallow that details of the bottom can be seen distinctly.

Similar swamps and tidal inlets continue eastward along the coast for 25 miles, then grade into drier land on which low brush, only partly covering the ground, forms a pronounced linear design suggestive of wind action. Within another 10 miles the origin of this pattern became clear, as we came over a great belt of sand dunes [39] that stretches continuously along the coast for the next 40 miles, and with interruptions for at least 60 miles more.

The dunes indicate a strong wind from a northeasterly direction that blows the sand inland for many miles, except at intervals where it is stopped by lagoons parallel with the shore. The dunes form imperfect crescents joined at the ends, but the most striking feature is the remarkable herringbone pattern visible on the grassy flats between the dunes. The interdune pattern is similar in dimensions and in outline to that of the dunes, and probably represents the truncated edges of the steeply inclined fore-set beds of dunes that have migrated to new positions. The preservation of such features would seem to demand slight sinking of the land or some other condition that would permit truncation of the dunes above their original bases. Such an effect might be produced without change of level if the dunes had originally migrated into shallow water.

As we passed the outer edge of the delta of the Rio Parnaíba, glimpses through the clouds revealed that the surface of the coastal margin of the delta is also controlled by drifting sand and that the herringbone patterns are prominent. From the Parnaíba delta to near Camocim, a course 5 to

10 miles out to sea permitted only the observation that the coastal region is swampy, with many tidal inlets and with a fringe of sand dunes along much of the shore.

Camocim to Recife

Eastward from Camocim, to about 15 miles south of Fortaleza, the route lay 15 to 30 miles inland, at first near the inner border of a sandy coastal plain, then over an old-age landscape of ancient rocks surmounted by widely scattered monadnocks and isolated mountain masses generally composed of granitic rocks.

East of Camocim it became evident at once that we were entering the dry region of northeastern Brazil, for the jungle became open and brushy, as in Figure 40, 15 miles S. 70°E. of Camocim. It is sparsely inhabited by people who practice shifting culture such as that shown in the photograph, where light-colored recent clearings or deadenings, enclosed by brush fences, are surrounded by abandoned fields in all stages of reversion to jungle. Cotton appeared to be the principal crop.

Farther eastward as we leave the coastal plain the amount of cultivated land increases somewhat, but shifting culture still prevails. A typical landscape is shown in Figure 41, about 60 miles S. 65°E. from Camocim. Native vegetation is everywhere of a brushy type, becoming lower and more open eastward. Scattered small monadnock hills appear, some of them, as in the upper right of the picture, composed of bedded rock dipping at a considerable angle westward and having a bluish-white color suggesting limestone or marble.

Greater detail of a characteristic landscape is shown in Figure 42, taken 10 miles farther along the route. The streams are sandy, and most of them were dry (February 14). Open spaces are becoming larger than farther west, small areas that have once been cleared appear here and there, and trails are numerous. No graded roads have been seen since leaving Camocim.

The route crossed the northern end of Serra de Uruburetama. These are rough craggy mountains of an igneous type whose higher parts, where not exposing bare rock, are but sparsely covered by brush. Northeast of them the lowland drained by the Rio Curú resembles those shown in preceding pictures, but in and around the hills 25 to 30 miles southwest of

Fortaleza, a decided improvement was noted. The soil is red, native vegetation is more luxuriant, more of the land is cultivated, and graded roads appear.

A general idea of the better part of this area can be gained from Figure 43, looking southward from about 15 miles southwest of Fortaleza, at the northern end of Serra de Maranguape. A flying altitude of over 13,000 feet and considerable atmospheric haze did not favor photography, but the old-age character of the mountains, the extensive forests on their upper slopes, and the numerous farms and farm homes in the valleys, connected by graded roads, can be readily distinguished.

Between Camocim and Fortaleza, the view far to the south disclosed an open country with generally smooth old-age topography rising gradually toward monadnocks or isolated mountain masses that stand here and there as residuals above the general level. From a distance, much of the surface appeared to be covered by savanna, though it may possibly have been low brush instead.

From the position of Figure 43, the route was roughly S. 48°E. over Mossoró and Assú. Clouds prevented effective photography, but occasional glimpses of the ground revealed a terrain, vegetation, and culture essentially similar to that shown in Figures 40, 41, and 42. Many of the cleared areas appear to have been abandoned.

The region is obviously too dry for successful agriculture without irrigation. It is part of that extensive area in northeastern Brazil which, because of aridity, must depend mainly on grazing, and suffers periodically from droughts that cause great losses of cattle. The Brazilian government has undertaken the extensive construction of dams (mainly farther inland) for holding the water of the rainy season and making it available for stock and for irrigation.[6]

Most of the way from Camocim, clouds partly obscured the ground. To fly above them required an altitude of between 14,000 and 15,000 feet. In general, their tops were billowy and of fairly uniform height, but here and there huge cumulus clouds, similar to those in Figure 8, rose to greater heights.

On the eastern slopes of Serra do Bom Fim more intensive cultivation

---

[6] See Friedrich W. Freise: The Drought Region of Northeastern Brazil, *Geogr. Rev.*, Vol. 28, 1938, pp. 363–378.

than any previously seen in northeastern Brazil [44] indicates that the rainfall must be considerably heavier there than farther west, but, nevertheless, everything appeared dry and burned. Patches of brush were dark, but not noticeably green, and the fields showed no green crops. Apparently the rains had not yet begun. The prinicipal crop appeared to be cotton. The next 25 miles of the route, over lower country in the valley of the Rio Trairí ou Camaropim, revealed brush land similar to that farther west, with only scattered cleared patches—evidence that cultivation hereabouts is restricted mainly to the higher slopes.

From near 6°20′ S., 35°52′ W. the course was changed to about S. 33°E. toward Recife, passing for the first 40 miles over a northeastern corner of the Brazilian highland—the plateau of Borborema [45, 46, 47]. The local relief is moderate, probably ranging from 300 to about 800 feet. The topography is late mature to old. Over much of the area distinct ridges trend between east and northeast [45, 46], but elsewhere the ridge form is lacking and the rock appears to be granitic. The plateau is mainly cleared, except on the higher and steeper hills. Native vegetation of a brush type occurs on the lower land and forest on the higher. The population is relatively dense, and roads may be distinguished. Even here the land was dry and brown in mid-February. Cotton seemed to be an important crop, mandioca is grown extensively, and general farming appears to be practiced. Much of the landscape is reminiscent of the Allegheny Plateau in West Virginia.

Within 5 or 6 miles of the site of Figure 47 we came out over a sandy coastal plain, its gray soil contrasting strongly with the red of the plateau. Well graded gravel roads lead toward João Pessoa (Paraíba), but in general the western edge of the coastal plain is much less developed than the plateau. Much of it is covered with brush.

Storm clouds obscured the eastern portion of the coastal plain as we approached Recife.

30. Morning fog lifting over forests typical of western Maranhão, about 190 miles east of Belém (NNE, from ca. 1°53′ S., 45°49′ W.)

31. The Rio Turiassú bordered by mangrove thickets and savannas (N, from ca. 1°59′ S., 45°16′ W.)

32. Lakes on the flood plain of the Rio Turiassú (SW, from ca. 1°59′ S., 45°15′ W.)

33. Alluvium of the Rio Turiassú flood plain "drowning" a low forested hill land (N, from ca. 1°59′ S., 45°14′ W.)

34. Shifting agriculture in the forests of Maranhão, about 57 miles northwest of São Luiz (S, from ca. 2°3′ S., 44°59′ W.)

35. Savanna and an unmapped estuary, probably the head of Baía de Cuman (S, from ca. 2°7′ S., 44°42′ W.)

36. Fish traps near the mouth of a tidal inlet, about 32 miles northwest of São Luiz (S, from 2°9′ S., 44°34′ W.)

37. Cliffed coast near Ponta Itacolomí, about 23 miles north-northwest of São Luiz (S, from 2°11′ S., 44°24′ W.)

38. Shoals and marshy coast along the east side of Baía de São José, 25 miles northeast of São Luiz (S, from 2° 19′ S., 43° 46′ W.)

39. Sand dunes along the coast about 75 miles east-northeast of São Luiz (N, from 2° 27′ S., 43° 12′ W.). The pattern indicates steady northeast winds

40. Shifting cultivation in typical brushy jungle, 15 miles east-southeast of Camocim (SW, from 3°0′ S., 40°34′ W.)

41. Partly cleared semiarid brush land typical of large areas in northern Brazil (SW, from ca. 3°17′ S., 39°58′ W.)

42. A dry stream bed, trails, and a few clearings in open brush land, 70 miles south-southeast of Camocim (SW, from ca. 3°22′ S., 39°51′ W.)

43. Farm lands at the base of the forested northern end of Serra de Maranguape, about 18 miles southwest of Fortaleza (SW, from 3°52′ S., 38°40′ W.)

44. Farm lands on the eastern slopes of Serra do Bom Fim, a portion of the plateau of northeastern Brazil (NE, from ca. 6°7′ S., 36°9′ W.)

45. Farm lands on low ridges of the Appalachian type on the Planalto da Borborema, about 123 miles northwest of Recife (SW, from ca. 6°33′ S., 35°44′ W.)

46. Ridges and cotton lands on the Planalto da Borborema, about 100 miles northwest of Recife (WSW, from ca. 6°49′ S., 35°34′ W.)

47. Old-age granitic (?) uplands of the Planalto da Borborema, about 95 miles northwest of Recife (SW, from ca. 6°53′ S., 35°31′ W.)

BRAZIL: RECIFE TO VITÓRIA*

Recife to Salvador

A DAWN take-off from Recife prevented a photographic record of the first 60 miles of the route. Ten miles south of the city the shore is bordered by a recent, narrow, swampy coastal plain, the seaward margin of which is lined with coconut groves. Inland, an elevated and dissected coastal plain of soft red rocks extends back some 20 miles to the edge of the plateau of crystalline rock, which, with an elevation ranging up to nearly 3000 feet, forms the western sky line all along the northern half of the eastern coast of Brazil. About 13 miles south of Recife the higher coastal plain extends down to the shore.

The general character of the dissected coastal plain is shown in Figure 48, 63 miles from Recife. The local relief is 100 to 200 feet or more. The topography is generally post-mature near the coast and more youthful inland. The flat valley bottoms are the seat of most of the cultivation, which, as in this photograph, is predominantly sugar. However, rice was noted in places, as well as what appeared to be general farming. The uplands are generally uncleared or show scattered clearings of shifting culture. The native vegetation is brush rather than forest. Similar landscape and culture continue to Maceió.

Thirty-two miles south of Maceió a view northward across the coastal plain [49] shows a youthful surface of moderate relief covered with low scrub in which an occasional clearing may be seen. The two bodies of water in the valley bottoms at the right are probably branches of Lagoa de Jiquiá. This is one of a series of such lakes that have been produced by recent submergence of the land drowning the youthful valleys, thus forming bays which were later converted into lakes by the coastal sand bars built across their mouths.[1]

About 9 miles farther on, a rich valley bottom a mile or two wide is extensively planted to sugar. Here, as everywhere since Recife, sugar is grown only on the flat, generally narrow, valley bottoms, and individual plantations do not appear to be large.

---

* See Maps III and IV, pp. 283 and 284, below.
[1] See Pierre Denis: Amérique du Sud (Géographie Universelle, Vol. 15), 2 parts, Paris, 1927, Part 1, p. 94.

As the delta of the Rio São Francisco is approached, the edge of the
elevated coastal plain recedes from the shore, which is composed of recent sediments brought down by the river and reworked by the waves.
Figure 50, looking westward from about 7 miles inland, shows the
broader features of the northern half of the delta. At the lower left a
series of white beach ridges appear sketchily through brushy jungle.
More than 15 of these are visible in the picture, and many more lie farther
seaward, all trending parallel to the present shore. Behind the ridges is an
ancient offshore sand bar, recognizable by the characteristic distribution
of patches of brush upon it. Beyond, lies a former lagoon, now mostly
grassy swamp, but showing outlines of former meandering tidal inlets.
On the far side of the lagoon, passing diagonally through the center of
the picture, is a gently curving line that may be interpreted as a low
wave-cut cliff, and behind that, what appears to be the typical youthfully
dissected coastal plain. The Rio São Francisco is visible in the background with the city of Penedo dimly discernible on its near bank to
the right of the center line. Villa Nova appears on the far bank, slightly
to the left.

Figure 51 shows additional features of the lower course of the Rio São
Francisco. Numerous islands and shoals suggest a heavy load of sediment.
Penedo, about 13 miles away (near center of picture) on a promontory
projecting into the river, seems to mark the upstream limit of the delta,
for the city has been mapped as lying on rock (Triassic?),[2] and dissected
coastal-plain topography appears beyond the river bank on the left side
of the picture. In the foreground are the swamps and abandoned meanders of the recent flood plain and delta.

Beyond the São Francisco delta we flew 3 to 5 miles offshore for the
next hundred miles. In that stretch we passed the mouths of four large-
sized streams, each showing estuarine features and extensive tidal flats.
Strips of light-yellow dunes border parts of the coast, and bands of
multiple beach ridges like those in Figure 50 were also noted north of
Aracajú and south of the Rio Irapuanga (11°11′ S.). The soils behind the
coastal belt appeared to be generally white, and the vegetation suggests
that they are sandy.

----

[2] J. C. Branner: The Geology of the Coast of the State of Alagôas, Brazil, *Annals
Carnegie Museum*, Vol. 7, 1910–1911, pp. 5–22.

Tall cumulus clouds of the type already repeatedly mentioned [8, 23, 26] formed in a belt along this part of the coast. A stereoscopic picture [156] shows much better than can an ordinary view, the beauty of form and shading in these towering cloud masses.[3] At the left, the higher cumuli, at about 10,000 feet, have been caught in a strong southerly wind and dragged out to leeward, but below that critical level the clouds must have been rising in calm air for they show no distortion.

A view inland [52] from close to the coast at a position 12°S. shows characteristic features of the coastal belt in that latitude. The relief is low, with late mature to old rounded forms, and streams wander across the flats in intricate meanders. Most of the ground is uncleared, but locally rather extensive orchards of palms, presumably coconut groves, may be seen, as in the area to the left of the center of the photograph. Some of the trees are planted in rows, but most are not. The absence of roads and the weak expression of trails or other evidences of human occupation indicate that coconut orcharding here cannot be very intensive. Perhaps this is an abandoned plantation. (For several miles back along the route coconut groves had been noted close to the shore.)

Three miles farther on, a view inland from over the coast line [53] shows a somewhat different but broadly similar aspect of the coastal belt. The characteristic rounded, late mature low relief of the coastal plain is well illustrated. The valley bottoms seem to have been alluviated somewhat, perhaps as a result of recent slight submergence. The soil appears to be very sandy. The vegetation is brushy, and here and there traces of small clearings may be seen. No roads or trails are visible.

Seventeen miles beyond the last picture, Figure 54 shows a similar terrain. The coast, marked by a line of breakers, appears in the upper part of the view. Immediately inland are partly bare sand hills, while farther inland is the low, rounded topography and sandy soil already described. This picture suggests that the alluviation of the valleys, noted also in the preceding picture, may be the result of the damming action of sand piled across the river mouths by wind from the sea.

---

[3] If the reader does not possess one of the newer pocket stereoscopes, the old-fashioned parlor stereoscope can be used, provided the book is laid on the edge of a table in such a way that the projecting print-holder will not interfere with bringing the lens to the proper distance.

One cannot fly along this sandy coast, with its onshore winds, without being impressed with the idea that almost the whole region might readily be converted into a great coconut grove. Coconuts are now grown here and there, but if a market were available and roads were provided so that the products could be assembled, the region would seem to have enormous possibilities.

For the next 50 miles, or to within 20 miles of Salvador, a topography similar to that of the preceding pictures was noted, with the same light-colored soil. The native vegetation is mainly low scrub and bunch brush. Locally there is considerable clearing of a desultory sort, but large areas seem almost untouched. Graded roads appear as Salvador is approached. Figure 55, looking westward from 20 miles N. 40°E. of Salvador, shows a similar topography and vegetation in the foreground except that larger trees are beginning to appear. In the background are the branching bays along the east side of Baía de Todos os Santos, forming a typical drowned topography with a relief of 200 to somewhat over 300 feet.

Salvador to Vitória

To the airplane passenger taking off southward, Salvador appears as a beautiful city perched on a generally flat-topped promontory some 200 feet above island-studded Baía de Todos os Santos to the west. Our plane took a straight course toward Canavieiras 185 miles to the south, which carried us from 15 to 20 miles offshore for the first 125 miles; consequently not much was seen of that part of the coast. The Ilha Maraú at latitude 14°S. appears to be a great sand bar whose form indicates prevailing shore currents from the south. Immediately south of the mouth of the sandy Rio das Contas (14°23′S.), which shows no obvious indication of drowning such as that at Salvador, a hilly land with a relief of about 400 feet extends out to the coast. Around Ilhéus it was noted that low hills of the dissected coastal plain reach the shore, and the land is mostly wooded or brush-covered with scattered patches of clearing. Similar topography and culture continue for at least 14 miles to the south.

Nine miles offshore at 15°8′S., and extending south for 12 miles, we flew over a remarkable display of bright golden-yellow to carrot-colored floating marine algae [56], lying approximately along a rather sharp line of demarcation between greenish water near the shore and deep blue water farther out—possibly a boundary between two opposing currents. Similar algae had been noted earlier at the entrance of the bay opposite Salvador.

Eleven miles north of Canavieiras, in latitude 15°31′S., Figure 57 shows that the low hill land bordering the shore for many miles south of Ilhéus has given way to a sand bar-lagoon type of coast—doubtless a result of progradation by sediment carried northward by shore currents from the mouths of the rivers Pardo and Jequitinhonha which enter the ocean a few miles farther south. Behind the lagoon, rather extensive coconut groves were noted, and beyond them the low hills of the dissected coastal plain mostly covered with forest or brushy jungle.

The town and surroundings of Canavieiras [58] illustrate an aspect of the coastal belt where rapid alluviation is in progress and where conditions seem decidedly unfavorable for human habitation. The Rio Pardo, on which the town is situated, and the Rio Jequitinhonha, visible at the extreme upper left, are evidently carrying heavy loads of sediment to the sea and adding to the land area, for a belt of old sea beaches 4 to 6 miles inland can be seen parallel to the coast between the two rivers (extending to the left from the center of the picture). Between the old beaches and the coast is a low area of tidal marshes, oxbow lakes, and lagoons, separated from the ocean by a dune-covered sand bar that deflects the Rio Pardo southward before it enters the ocean. Behind the old beaches, a meandering, marsh-bordered channel that may be seen branching off to the left from the Rio Pardo four miles from the coast connects with the Rio Jequitinhonha. All of these features constitute a swampy and undoubtedly unhealthful coastal strip 5 to 10 or so miles wide. Farther back the land is low and hilly.

Outside the town very little evidence of cultivation or habitation can be discerned. Boats may be seen on the river, and what is probably an airplane landing field appears at the right. Canavieiras, and other towns along the coast, are mainly shipping ports for cacao.

By flying offshore from Salvador to Canavieiras we failed to see anything of the cacao industry, which, centered mainly in the rain forests in the foothills west of Ilhéus, but extending less intensively all the way from near Salvador southward to the Rio Doce, gives Brazil second place in world cacao production. The cacao tree thrives only on the residual soils produced by the decomposition of the crystalline rocks of the hin-

terland, or on river flood plains and terraces composed of material derived from them, and consequently cacao culture approaches the coast
only along some of the larger rivers, especially the Rio Pardo and the
Rio Jequitinhonha.[4]

Along the south side of the delta of the Rio Jequitinhonha, from Belmonte at the river mouth southward for many miles, is a remarkable display of multiple beach ridges well illustrated by Figure 59. We are looking
steeply down toward the ocean, where the line of surf may be recognized
along the top of the picture. The beach ridges are very closely spaced,
with narrow swamps and one broad lagoon between them. They are so
striking that they excite much interest among air passengers flying over
them.

For more than 50 miles south from Canavieiras the old beach lines are
almost continuous. In places, as south of Belmonte, they extend for miles
as long, straight embankments of white sand, but on projecting points
like Ponta Grande [60] (16°22′ S.), they record graphically the effects
of conflicting currents and show clearly how the point has grown out-
ward from an old wave-cut cliff that may be seen in the foreground,
separating a brushy, low, hilly land from the sand-covered plain. Under
water offshore, a shoal on which the waves are breaking shows points
extending both north (left) and south built by currents from first one
direction and then the other, carrying sand along the front of the shoal
and dumping it into deeper water at the ends.

Between Belmonte at the mouth of the Rio Jequitinhonha and Ponta
Grande, the region back from the coast is a gently rolling plain rising
gradually inland. Where not covered by dense, brushy scrub and jungle,
a white infertile soil appears. Shifting culture is practiced in scattered
patches in the jungle. Figure 61 was taken steeply down over the region
close to the coast, 15 miles south of Ponta Grande. Partly open brushy
land like this grades inland into jungle. No signs of habitation or of
clearings appear.

In striking contrast with the prograded coast south of Belmonte is a
stretch of cliffed coast [62], noted for more than 35 miles between 16°43′
and 17°12′ S. In this region waves have worn the coast line back for a

---

[4] For an excellent account of cacao in Brazil see Pierre Monbeig: Colonisation, peuple-
ment et plantation de cacao dans le sud de l'état de Bahia, *Ann. de Géogr.*, Vol. 46, 1937,
pp. 278–299.

considerable distance. Truncated former headlands may be seen as shoals beneath the water, as in the left half of the photograph. In some of the reëntrants between the larger headlands multiple beach ridges were observed, but it seems probable that they have been produced by prograding rather than by uplift. What resembles a road a short distance back from the shore follows the route of a telegraph line shown on the map.

Beginning a few miles north of Caravelas (17°43' S.), the appearance of the coastal plain becomes entirely different from anything seen farther north. Its character is well shown in Figure 63, looking west-northwest from about 6 miles south of that town. Brushy jungle has given way to open, grassy plains with brush occurring only along drainage courses and around peculiar rounded depressions on the divides or at stream heads. These are similar to the depressions noted in Ceará, and to features commonly shown on aerial photographs of southern coastal Texas.

About 5 miles to the south, brushy jungle with scattered small clearings, such as that common along most of the coast farther north, reappears. Multiple beach ridges, similar to those of Figure 59, and barrier beaches and lagoons feature the coast for the next 130 miles to and across the large, lake-studded delta of the Rio Doce. Parts of the delta are so young as to be almost bare of vegetation, but elsewhere brushy jungle occupies much of the surface. Portions of it have scattered clearings.

About 5 miles south of the southern limit of the delta of the Rio Doce, Figure 64 shows the rolling, dissected coastal plain extending to the edge of the water. Along its margin is a low, but distinctly elevated, wave-cut platform 1000 to 1500 feet wide, backed by a fossil wave-cut cliff. Valley bottoms are flat and grassy, as near the center of the photograph. Corn or sugar cane is planted in small patches on the uplands.

About 4 miles farther on, a view inland over Santa Cruz (to the left of the center) shows a curious combination of physiographic features [65]. The broad estuary and the wide river flats indicate drowning, while a narrow elevated platform and fossil wave-cut cliff a few hundred yards back from the shore in the foreground indicate slight emergence, as in the preceding picture. The untrenched condition of the river flats suggests that sinking has been the more recent of the two movements. In the background may be seen the granitic hills that come out to the coast near Vitória.

Santa Cruz is the site of a recently projected port to serve as the terminus of a railway leading up the natural highway of the Rio Doce to the great iron ore deposits of Minas Gerais.[5]

Close to the coast, 4 miles south of Santa Cruz [66], the coastal plain of low relief has been partially drowned and its valley bottoms wholly or partly filled with alluvium and converted into grassy swamps. Patches of brush and scattered trees appear to be the original vegetation rather than second growth, and only a few faint trails suggest human occupation.

The sunken and partly alluviated character of the coastal region north of Vitória is even better shown in Figure 67, looking westward from about 18 miles north-northeast of that city. An old land surface of slight relief appears to have been dissected by streams to early maturity, then submerged. Rivers are gradually filling the ends of the branching bays. In the background rise outliers of granitic mountains.

About 13 miles before Vitória is reached, a view to the west-north-west [68] shows at the right the old-age lowland already mentioned, surmounted by scattered monadnocks of granitic rock weathered into smooth, rounded domes such as those in the middle distance, and in the far background the edge of the great Brazilian Plateau.[6] The road at the right is the first well graded one seen since leaving Salvador. In the foreground the vegetation displays a preference for south-facing slopes.

Summary — Recife to Vitória

Flying from Recife to Vitória along the east coast of Brazil, one is impressed by the generally undeveloped condition of the coastal belt. Except for occasional port towns serving the interior, and except for coconut groves here and there, little can be seen to indicate human activity aside from scattered small clearings in brushy jungle. Roads and trails are almost entirely lacking, so that there is generally no means of land travel from one place to another along the coast. Railroads and roads, however, run inland from the various ports tapping important

---

[5] Preston E. James: Notes on a Journey up the Valley of the Rio Doce, Brazil, *Journ. of Geogr.,* Vol. 32, 1933, pp. 98–107.

[6] Here and in the following chapter the term "plateau" is used in the popular sense of an upland of relatively even surface, rather than in the more limited physiographic sense of an upland underlain by horizontal strata.

resource areas. Ilhéus, for example, is one of the principal outlets for the second largest cacao producing region in the world.

The coastal plain, lying between the Brazilian Plateau and the sea, is in general sufficiently elevated for reasonably good drainage and has been more or less maturely dissected by streams. Its topography as a rule is not unfavorable, but along much of the route the soil appears to be sandy and infertile. Long stretches of the coast are swampy where excessive sediment carried down by the major streams has caused a relatively recent extension of the land area, as at Canavieiras [58], but as a rule the swampy belt is relatively narrow. A notable exception is the huge delta of the Rio Doce. Because of the equatorial latitude, the coastal lowland is undoubtedly hot and naturally unhealthful, but mosquito control has done wonders, as for example at Recife.

To the layman it would seem that the east coast of Brazil could readily produce all the coconut products that would ever be needed in the western hemisphere.

48. Sugar plantations in valleys of the dissected coastal plain southwest of Recife (ESE, from 8°53′ S., 35°15′ W.)

49. The youthfully dissected, brush-mantled surface of the coastal plain 33 miles southwest of Maceió (N, from 10°0′ S., 36°3′ W.)

50. Elevated beaches along the north side of the Rio São Francisco delta (W, from 10°22′ S., 36°23′ W.). The river can be seen in the background

51. Looking up the Rio São Francisco from a position about 7 miles inland (NW, from 10°26′ S., 36°26′ W.)

52. Coastal plain with coconut groves, as seen from a point over the shore line (NW, from 11°59′ S., 37°39′ W.)

53. The sandy, jungle-covered coastal plain with its characteristically alluviated valleys, about halfway between Aracajú and Salvador (NW, from 12°1′ S., 37°40′ W.)

54. The seaward margin of the coastal plain 70 miles northeast of Salvador (SE, from 12° 13′ S., 37° 50′ W.)

55. Looking over the coastal plain to the drowned valleys at the head of Baía de Todos os Santos, 18 miles northeast of Salvador (W, from 12° 46′ S., 38° 19′ W.)

56. Floating yellow marine algae about 9 miles offshore and 150 miles south of Salvador (W, from 15°12′ S., 38°53′ W.)

57. A view typical of the coast and coastal plain about 11 miles north of Canavieiras (W, from 15°31′ S., 38°55′ W.)

58. The coastal plain and old beach lines (SW, from 15°39' S., 38°56' W.). Canavieiras appears in the foreground and the Rio Jequitinhonha in the left background

59. Old beach ridges along the shore on the southern side of the Rio Jequitinhonha delta, 19 miles south of Canavieiras (E, from 15°57' S., 38°58' W.)

60. Elevated beach ridges and an old shore line at Ponta Grande, 46 miles south of Canavieiras (ESE, from 16°22′ S., 39°3′ W.)

61. Typical brushy vegetation near the shore of the coastal plain about 61 miles south of Canavieiras (W, from 16°34′ S., 39°5′ W.)

62. A cliffed coast about 67 miles north of Caravelas (W, from 16°46′ S., 39°6′ W.)

63. The grass-covered coastal plain west of Caravelas (WNW, from 17°48′ S., 39°18′ W.)

64. The coastal plain, marked by alluviated valleys and an elevated sea cliff, about 7 miles northeast of Santa Cruz (W, from 19°52′ S., 40°2′ W.)

65. The harbor and surroundings of Santa Cruz (W, from 19°55′ S., 40°4′ W.). The estuary is bordered by an elevated sea cliff

66. Alluviated valleys on the coastal plain about 3 miles southwest of Santa Cruz (WNW, from 19°59′ S., 40°7′ W.)

67. Drowned valleys about 18 miles north-northeast of Vitória (W, from 20°5′ S., 40°11′ W.)

BRAZIL: VITÓRIA TO SÃO PAULO*

Vitória to Rio de Janeiro

IN THE vicinity of Vitória, a local peneplain or old-age erosion surface standing about 200 feet above the sea and developed on crystalline rocks, extends as a terrace of varying width along the base of the Brazilian highland and penetrates for a considerable distance into it along some of the larger valleys, such as that of the Rio Itapemirim and the Rio Itabapoana. The old erosion surface has been rather sharply trenched by streams, then lowered enough to permit the sea to enter the valleys. Most of the drowned valleys have been alluviated, but one that has not yet been filled forms the beautiful harbor on which Vitória is located. The shore lines of the bay around Vitória show angular features presumably caused by the erosional etching of fracture patterns in the crystalline rock.

Clear weather permitted use of a direct route across the mountains from Vitória to Rio de Janeiro instead of the longer route along the coast. Fifteen miles southwest of Vitória, Figure 69 shows in the foreground a typical section of the partial peneplain or terrace described above, and in the background the generally even-topped, maturely dissected eastern edge of the Brazilian Plateau somewhat over 3000 feet in height. That the region supports a moderately dense agricultural population, is evident from Figure 70, showing the valley of a small stream a mile farther on. Among the recognizable crops were sugar cane, corn, and bananas.

Looking south and forward toward the sea, from 20 miles southwest of Vitória [71], one sees granitic knobs rising as residuals above the old-age surface. A good deal of the lower land seems to be devoted to pasture, the higher land on the mountain slopes evidently being preferred for cultivation, as may be seen in succeeding pictures.

Seven miles farther along, a view northwestward from the opposite side of the plane [72] shows the eastern slopes of Serra da Independencia, a spur of the plateau that comes relatively close to the coast. The mountains support a dense tropical forest and many of the slopes have

* See Map IV, p. 284, below.

been cleared, though some of them are excessively steep. The population is fairly dense.

The details of culture along the inner edge of the coastal peneplain are well shown by Figure 73, about 45 miles southwest of Vitória and 8 miles inland. The relief is moderate and the land well cleared and rather densely settled. The farm homes appear on the photograph as white spots representing bare ground where the vegetation has been removed around each house. Near the center of the picture a lens will reveal that most of the cleared ground is occupied by low trees planted in rows—probably coffee. Bananas, corn, sugar cane, and other crops were also noted. The land appears to be fertile, and the farms are generally well cared for. This region was colonized during the last century by Germans, and later by Italians. These peoples constitute a considerable part of the population in the neighborhood of the Rio Itapemirim and the Rio Itabapoana.

From the position of this picture, the old-age land surface slopes gradually down toward the sea. It also extends far up the valley of the Rio Itapemirim and its tributaries. Looking down on a portion of it near that river, which appears in the upper right of Figure 74, one sees a subdued, late-mature landscape of very moderate relief, characterized by peculiar rounded forms such as have been conspicuous on all the pictures of this surface south of Santa Cruz. Drowning has caused alluviation and, apparently, ponding of tributary valleys such as that in the foreground. These show no stream channels and their flat bottoms are covered with swamp grass. Such terrain is almost uninhabited, in strong contrast to the higher ground of the preceding pictures.

Among the crystalline rocks that underlie all of the region over which we have flown since leaving Santa Cruz, are numerous cores, or unbroken, unjointed masses of granitic[1] rock, that are extremely resistant to weathering and consequently remain high while the surrounding rocks are eroded away. These granitic cores are responsible for one of the most striking features of the landscape of the Brazilian highlands all the way from Vitória to and beyond Rio de Janeiro—the great domes or "sugar loaves" of which Pão d'Azucar and Corcovado at Rio de Janeiro are the best known. Similar mountains in the United States, formed

---

[1] The word "granitic" is used here in a broad sense; composition may be monzonitic.

in the same way, are Stone Mountain in Georgia, Mount Cadillac in Acadia National Park, Maine, and Mount Rushmore in the Black Hills of South Dakota.

Figure 75 shows such a dome in the Serra do Sapateiro, rising abruptly out of the lowland immediately north of the Rio Paraíba do Sul. The dimensions of the vertical granite cliffs may be gauged by comparison with the giant tropical trees that cling precariously to the slopes below. In the right background, the landscape is similar to that in Figure 73.

A view up the valley of the Rio Paraíba do Sul [76], from over a point 7 miles below the town of São Fidelis (on the river bank to the right of the center), shows a late-mature to old-age surface, continuous with that already described, bordering the river and merging gradually with higher ground on either side. A short distance above São Fidelis may be seen the first of a series of rapids that block navigation, but which constitute an important potential water-power resource, for the Paraíba do Sul is a large river draining an area of considerable rainfall.

After crossing the valley of the Rio Paraíba do Sul, our route followed over the summit of the highlands between that valley and Rio de Janeiro. The succeeding pictures should convey a clear idea of the intensive mountain culture that has developed in these highlands, mainly as a result of the coffee industry. About 25 miles south-southwest of São Fidelis, a typical section of the highland is well shown [77]. A neat mountain village served by good roads gives ample evidence that something more than subsistence agriculture is being practiced in the vicinity. Some 8 miles farther on [78] the exceedingly winding course of a railroad grade—which, to judge from the photograph, may have been converted into a motor road—testifies to the difficulties encountered in providing means of exporting the valuable products of these high mountain valleys. In the center, a white square suggests the probable site of the drying platform of a coffee fazenda; and here, as in all the other pictures of the region, a white spot at the end of a trail marks a mountain home.

For another 8 miles, to the position of Figure 79, the topography and culture continue to be essentially the same as in the two preceding pictures. Here the land was close enough to our flying level for more details of the culture to be discernible. We are looking steeply down at the head of a mountain valley in which what presumably is coffee is intensively grown. The trees are scarcely visible on the scale of the photograph, but on the enlargement (inserted at the upper left) of the area within the dotted rectangle, the rows of trees are readily distinguishable. At least five more or less rectangular white areas, presumably coffee drying floors, may be recognized.

Another view [80], 4 miles farther along the route, and approximately 79 miles N. 54°E. of Rio de Janeiro, shows not only a representative example of mountain culture in this area, but also several of the granite domes typical of the region. The Brazilians call them *meia laranjas*, meaning "half oranges."

The railroad of Figure 78, serving as an outlet to a market, probably accounts in part for the particularly intensive culture for the past 20 miles of the route. From the air this intensively cultivated mountain region is exceptionally beautiful, with its varied shades of green, brilliant in the afternoon sun, and with here and there a tree in the forest setting off the green with its red, purple, or orange-yellow blossoms. Not alone from the air, this portion of Brazil is perhaps one of the most lovely parts of the world. From the ground it is equally attractive [82]. This view near Petrópolis shows essentially the same type of landscape as that of the preceding pictures, including the steep-walled granite domes and the clearings in the valleys.

For the next 20 miles beyond the site of Figure 80 the topography is generally similar to that already illustrated, but the culture gradually becomes somewhat less intensive. Fifty-five miles northeast of Rio de Janeiro we look westward [81], over the rugged, forested mountains in the foreground to where, beyond 35 miles of sharp mountain ridges and deep intervening valleys, the huge granite "fingers" (Dedo de Deus) of the Serra dos Orgãos, or Organ Mountains, rise in intriguing outlines against the western sky.

After the flight across the mountains from Vitória, the distinctive topography for which the harbor of Rio de Janeiro is famous [83], with its rounded granite domes and towering spines, is readily recognized as characteristic of all the highland south of Vitória; but here it happens to have been half submerged by the sinking of the outer border of the highland. The picture was taken from Corcovado, one of the spines;

another, Sugarloaf or Pão d'Azucar, rising 1230 feet above the bay, appears to the right of the center. On the lower land between the domes and on the bay-head flats, behind a festoon of crescent beaches, stands the city of Rio de Janeiro on a site of unrivaled natural beauty.

Rio de Janeiro to São Paulo

On a clear morning, early enough so that shadows served to emphasize relief, we flew northwestward from Rio de Janeiro to the western side of Baía de Guanabara, thence taking a straight course S. 76°W. toward São Paulo. For the first half of the distance, the route lay mainly over the ocean close to the rugged escarpment of Serra do Mar, and for the last half, over the plateau 15 to 30 miles inland.

The lowland occupied in part by Baía de Guanabara, covering an area roughly 30 miles square west and northwest of Rio de Janeiro, is an old-age surface of crystalline rocks locally veneered with alluvium and surmounted by several monadnock mountain masses. About 25 miles west of Rio de Janeiro [84] parts of this lowland, and sections of the rounded hills rising above it, are utilized for intensive orcharding. Oranges are said to be of leading importance.

From the same locality a broader view north-northeastward [85] shows the lowland, with a knobby surface characteristic of old age on crystalline rocks, surmounted by low monadnock ridges having a pronounced northeast trend, and at wider intervals by larger monadnock mountain masses. In the right background are the mountains near Petrópolis.

A view northward about 39 miles west of Rio de Janeiro [86] reveals the fact that the northeastern end of the coastal range divides into two relatively straight-fronted ranges, apparently fault slivers, of which the nearer plunges down beneath the lowland west of Rio de Janeiro at the center of the picture, and the farther sinks less steeply to the low pass between that lowland and the Paraíba Valley behind the second range. In the foreground are lagoons along the shore line and a mangrove thicket covering part of an alluvial plain in front of the nearer range.

About 8 miles farther west, south of the route, is an interesting example of the work of waves and shore currents [87]. This view shows part of Restinga da Marambaia, a barrier beach 25 miles in length, which ties Ilha da Marambaia, a short distance to the right, with the mainland.

At an earlier stage in the growth of the barrier, a large hook was formed, and the successive growth lines of this feature are visible to the left of the center. Later, the small island in the foreground was tied to the end of the hook by a narrow, crooked bar of sand partly under water. Open ocean appears at the top of the picture. In the lagoon behind the bar the bottom, everywhere visible beneath the water, displays an interesting pattern.

From over the center of Baía de Sepetiba, 51 miles in an air line from Rio de Janeiro, Figure 88 gives a clear impression of the physiography to the north. In the foreground Serra Morro de Itaguaí rises steeply about 3500 feet above the ocean. Beyond the range, a maturely dissected hilly land slopes gradually down to the Rio Paraíba valley, near the fog bank in the upper center of the picture. Faraway on the sky line is a high escarpment beyond the Paraíba trough.

Eighteen miles farther west, Figure 89 fairly represents the nature of the intervening coast range. Maturely dissected mountains rise abruptly from the water's edge. In the lower right moderate relief and smooth rounded forms suggest the presence of a coarse-grained intrusive rock such as granite, which characteristically weathers in such a manner. The more angular forms of the wooded mountains behind perhaps betray the occurrence of a more resistant rock. The region is obviously inaccessible except from the sea and appears to be only sparsely inhabited.

From over the eastern part of Baía da Ilha Grande, 70 miles west of Rio de Janeiro, a view northward [90] reveals most graphically the drowned nature of the topography that characterizes this portion of the Brazilian coast for hundreds of miles in either direction. Maturely dissected granitic mountains with characteristic domelike forms have been partly submerged by the sinking of the land. Steep slopes lead directly down to and below the water level, and outlying peaks appear as islands. Sinking has been so recent that no noticeable wave-cut cliffs have yet been formed on the headlands, although alluvium brought down by the streams has partly filled some of the bay heads, making good beaches and small areas of level land. At the left is the town and port of Angra dos Reis, joined by rail across the mountains with the main line in the Paraíba trough which connects Rio de Janeiro with São Paulo.

That the sinking responsible for the drowning of the coastal belt is due to faulting parallel to the coast is strongly suggested by Figure 91, looking approximately N. 70°E. over the head of Baía Ribeira, northwest of Angra dos Reis, appearing at the lower right. A relatively straight escarpment rises abruptly about 2500 feet to a pronounced shoulder at the seaward margin of an old-age erosion surface. This surface extends back several miles to a residual range forming the summit of the highlands south of the Paraíba trough, the axis of which is indicated by a belt of fog. Beyond the trough, the great south-facing escarpment of Serra da Mantiqueira forms the sky line about 60 miles away. It too is generally considered to be a fault scarp, marking the northwestern side of the Paraíba trough.

The geological recency of the drowning of the coastal area is clearly evident from such a picture as Figure 92, showing the peninsula, 3500 feet high, that ends at Cabo Joatinga. Its stream-carved sprawling mountain spurs, even on the points fully exposed to the Atlantic waves, have not been noticeably cliffed, though small crescent beaches have formed in many of the reëntrants. At the heads of some of the bays, entered by streams larger than those shown on the photograph, small alluvial plains and deltas have been built.

As the plane approached the crest of the escarpment pictured in Figure 91, at the point where it turns southward to parallel the western side of Baía da Ilha Grande, a view to the north [93] reveals clearly that the edge of the escarpment is encroaching northward on the maturely dissected upland of moderate relief already described. The escarpment is retreating nearly at right angles to the trend of the valleys on the upland, where some of the streams, not shown on the photograph, have already been captured and plunge as sheer falls and foaming rapids for hundreds of feet over the edge of the escarpment before disappearing in the forest. The hanging condition of such streams testifies to the geological recency of the escarpment.

Beyond the escarpment is an extensive maturely dissected plateau,[2] the form of which suggests that an erosion surface graded to a lower level at the left, is encroaching on a higher surface at the center and right (Serra da Bocaina). On the sky line, beyond the Paraíba trough, is one

---

[2] See above, note 6, page 50.

of the higher portions of Serra da Mantiqueira (including Morro Itati-
aía, 9353 feet).[3]

From over the southern edge of the plateau, 15 miles along the course
west of Baía da Ilha Grande, the view south-southeast to the coast [94]
reveals the maturely dissected seaward face of the escarpment to be
heavily forested, though part of the land on the lower valley slopes and
on the bay-head flats has apparently been cleared at some time. The
islands offshore give the impression of continuing the general seaward
slope of the escarpment face, as if the sinking had occurred after much
of the dissection of the escarpment had been accomplished. In this region, direct drainage to the Atlantic is limited to the seaward face of the
escarpment. Flowing west-southwestward parallel to the coast and less
than 10 miles from it for the upper 30 miles of its course, the Rio Paraïbuna
eventually turns northward into the Paraíba trough to enter the Atlantic
150 miles northeast of Rio de Janeiro, nearly 500 miles from its source.

The nature of the Brazilian Plateau 12 miles from the coast, and 25
miles west of Baía da Ilha Grande (about 102 miles in an easterly direction from São Paulo), is well illustrated in Figure 95. It is a maturely
dissected hill land having a relief of 300 or 400 feet and an altitude of
about 3500 feet. Like all of the highland between Rio de Janeiro and
São Paulo, it is underlain by ancient crystalline rocks which generally
are so nearly uniform in their resistance to erosion that they have not
interfered with the development of normal dendritic stream patterns.
The region appears never to have been completely forested, especially
on the hilltops and on the sun-bathed northern slopes. It seems to be
used mainly as pasture since, though it supports a moderate population,
not much evidence of cultivation is to be seen.

The plateau continues with similar topography to the very edge of
the Serra do Mar, which appears here simply as the escarpment edge
of the plateau. The only noticeable difference near the edge is that, for
a few miles back, the land is densely and completely forested in response
to the heavier rainfall occurring there (180 to 240 inches annually).

The topographic features illustrated in Figure 95, as well as in preced-

---

[3] For a discussion of transhumance on these higher mountains, and of mountain culture
in general in the highlands between here and Vitória, see Pierre Deffontaines: Mountain
Settlement in the Central Brazilian Plateau, *Geogr. Rev.*, Vol. 27, 1937, pp. 394–413.

ing pictures, have produced one of the greatest water-power resources
in the world. A plateau, 2500 to 3000 feet high, the streams of which
flow away from the near-by ocean on gradients gentle enough so that
dams of moderate height can store large volumes of water, falls off by
an abrupt drop to the sea not 5 miles away, and the rainfall is exceptionally heavy all along the seaward edge of the plateau. This power has
been partly developed in the remarkable Serra do Cubatão plant near
Santos, serving the São Paulo-Santos district. There, a dam (about 90
feet high) 18 miles from the edge of the plateau, serves to reverse the
water flow and permit a drop of over 2300 feet to the power plant at
the foot of the escarpment.[4]

Four miles beyond the site of the preceding picture, a broader view
northward across the plateau is afforded by Figure 96. A maturely dissected region of moderate relief stretches northward about 20 miles to
the broad Paraíba trough, beyond which the Serra da Mantiqueira rises
as an unbroken wall on the sky line. Thirteen miles farther west, and
about 84 miles east of São Paulo, a view [97] slightly east of north over
the village of São Luiz do Paraïtinga (near the center) shows the relation of one of the larger local streams to the topography of the maturely
dissected plateau. The main valley is not noticeably wider or more flat-
bottomed than that of its minor tributaries. In the nearer background a
pronounced escarpment, Serra da Quebra Cangalha,[5] abruptly inter-
rupts the generally accordant sky line of the plateau. Its straight course
and relatively steep front to the south suggest that it may be due to
faulting along a fracture roughly parallel to that generally conceded to
be responsible for the escarpment of Serra da Mantiqueira, visible on the
sky line beyond the Paraíba trough.

Details of typical vegetation and land use on the plateau 60 miles east
of São Paulo are revealed in Figure 98. South-facing slopes support

---

[4] A. W. K. Billings: Water Power in Brazil, *Civil Engineering*, Vol. 8, 1938, pp. 520–523.

[5] The Serra da Quebra Cangalha escarpment poses one of the several interesting physiographic problems suggested by preceding pictures. Some of them have been touched upon
in recent contributions to the physiography of the highlands of southern Brazil, notably:
Otto Maull: Die geomorphologischen Grundzüge Mittel-Brasiliens, *Zeitschr. Gesell. für
Erdkunde zu Berlin*, 1924, pp. 161–197; Otto Maull: Vom Itatiaya zum Paraguay: Ergebnisse
und Erlebnisse einer Forschungsreise durch Mittelbrazilien, Leipzig, 1930; Preston E. James:
The Surface Configuration of Southeastern Brazil, *Annals Assn. of Amer. Geogrs.*, Vol. 23,
1933, pp. 165–193; and Emmanuel de Martonne: Problèmes morphologiques du Brésil tropical atlantique, *Ann. de Géogr.*, Vol. 49, 1940, pp. 1–27 and 106–129.

dense forest, but north-facing slopes and rounded summits are generally grassy or covered with low brush. Small farms may be seen in the valleys. Corn patches were noted here and there, but cultivation is not intensive.

Similar topography and culture characterize the plateau for the next 30 miles along the route [99, 100]. Orcharding becomes noticeable, increasing westward. Blue-green patches proved to be groves of young eucalyptus, which are being planted extensively around São Paulo for fuel, timber, and oil. Because of the scarcity of coal, eucalyptus wood is widely used as fuel, for such services as powering small industrial establishments and for burning brick.

West of Mogí das Cruzes the topography became gently rolling and the relief considerably reduced as we left the crystalline rocks and came over the Tertiary sediments that fill the São Paulo basin and the bottom of the Paraíba trough. The general aspect of this region, as seen from the ground [101], is predominantly that of rolling, brushy grassland on which are found many market gardens (foreground) and orchards. Large termite mounds cover parts of the plain.

If we take a side trip to Santos, we find that southeast of São Paulo the plateau continues with a topography and culture similar to that farther east. Where the edge of the escarpment is reached, the land drops abruptly to the swampy, drowned lowland around Santos. A view to the northeast from a hill in that city [102] shows the 3000-foot escarpment in the background, the partly drowned hills of the down-dropped block in the middle distance, and the tidal estuary and alluvial plains on which Santos is situated in the foreground.

68. Granitic monadnocks and the distant edge of the Brazilian Plateau, about 13 miles northeast of Vitória (WNW, from 20°9′ S., 40°15′ W.). See page 50

69. Coastal peneplain or terrace and the edge of the plateau, 15 miles southwest of Vitória (NW, from ca. 20°27′ S., 40°29′ W.)

70. Landscape patterns about 16 miles southwest of Vitória (NW, from ca. 20°27′ S., 40°30′ W.)

71. Granitic monadnocks rising above the coastal terrace about 20 miles southwest of Vitória (S, from ca. 20°30′ S., 40°32′ W.)

72. Mountain agriculture on the eastern slopes of the Brazilian Plateau, 26 miles southwest of Vitória (NW, from ca. 20°34′ S., 40°36′ W.)

73. Densely settled hill lands along the eastern base of the Brazilian Plateau, about 45 miles southwest of Vitória (NW, from ca. 20°46′ S., 40°47′ W.)

74. Alluviated valleys and the sparsely settled lowland bordering the Rio Itapemirim (NNW, from ca. 20°58′ S., 40°58′ W.)

75. Serra do Sapateiro, a granite dome similar to Stone Mountain in Georgia, rising abruptly above the plain of the Rio Paraíba do Sul (NW, from ca. 21°37′ S., 41°35′ W.)

76. Looking up the Rio Paraíba do Sul over São Fidelis (WNW, from 21°41′ S., 41°38′ W.)

77. A mountain village in the coffee lands south of the Rio Paraíba do Sul (NW, from 22°1′ S., 41°56′ W.)

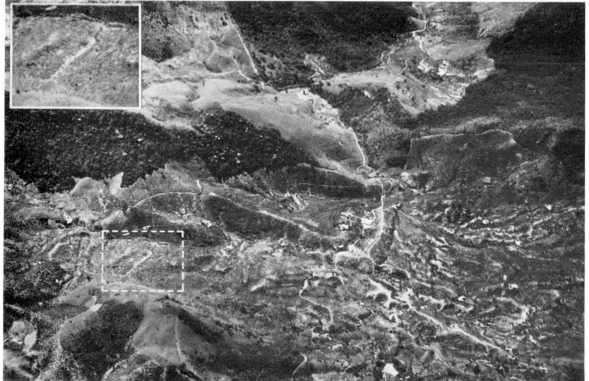

78. A railroad grade in a high mountain valley in the coffee country about 93 miles northeast of Rio de Janeiro (NW, from 22°7′ S., 42°1′ W.)

79. Coffee culture in a high valley about 85 miles northeast of Rio de Janeiro (NW, from 22°12′ S., 42°6′ W.)

80. Coffee culture and characteristic granite domes in the mountains about 79 miles northeast of Rio de Janeiro (NW, from 22°15′ S., 42°9′ W.)

81. The Serra dos Orgãos on the sky line, as seen from a point about 55 miles northeast of Rio de Janeiro (W, from ca. 22°29′ S., 42°25′ W.)

82. Mountains similar to those of the preceding pictures, as seen from the ground near Petrópolis (from ca. 22°32′ S., 43°10′ W.)

83. A view over Rio de Janeiro and its harbor from Corcovado peak (E)

84. Orchards on the hills about 22 miles west of Rio de Janeiro (N, from 22°54′ S., 43°37′ W.)

85. Monadnocks rising above the general level of the old-age topography west of Rio de Janeiro (NNE, from 22°54′30″ S., 43°37′30″ W.)

86. The divided northeastern end of the coastal range, as seen from a point over Baía de Sepetiba 39 miles west of Rio de Janeiro (N, from 22°57′ S., 43°47′ W.)

87. Ocean floor patterns and a developing hook at the western end of Restinga da Marambaia, an offshore bar 45 miles west of Rio de Janeiro (S, from 22°58′ S., 43°54′ W.)

88. Looking across the coastal range to the Paraíba trough, 51 miles west of Rio de Janeiro (N, from 22°59′ S., 43°58′ W.)

89. The seaward front of the coastal mountains 69 miles west of Rio de Janeiro (NNE, from 23°3′ S., 44°15′ W.)

90. Drowned topography typical of the coastal mountains east of Angra dos Reis (left) (N, from 23°4′ S., 44°17′ W.)

91. The drowned topography, coastal escarpment, and distant Paraíba trough near Angra dos Reis (lower right) (N, from 23°4′ S., 44°20′ W.)

92. The partly submerged mountain mass which terminates in Cabo Joatinga (SSE, from 23°8′ S., 44°37′ W.)

93. Looking across the coastal escarpment and the aligned structures behind it to the Serra da Mantiqueira in the background beyond the Paraíba trough, halfway between Rio de Janeiro and São Paulo (N, from 23°10′ S., 44°45′ W.)

94.   The forested coastal escarpment of the Serra do Mar, 112 miles east of São Paulo (SSE, from 23°13' S., 44°55' W.)

95.   A maturely dissected plateau of moderate relief at the top of the coastal escarpment, 102 miles east of São Paulo (N, from 23°14' S., 45°2' W.)

96. The maturely dissected plateau, the Paraíba trough, and the Serra da Mantiqueira on the sky line, as seen from a position 98 miles east of São Paulo (N, from 23°15′ S., 45°5′ W.)

97. A village on the plateau, an escarpment rising above the general level of the upland, and the Paraíba trough in the background, 84 miles east of São Paulo (N, from 23°17′ S., 45°17′ W.)

98. Topographic, vegetational, and cultural patterns on the plateau 60 miles east of São Paulo (N, from 23°21′ S., 45°40′ W.)

99. Topography and culture along the Rio Paraíba do Sul on the plateau 50 miles east of São Paulo (NNE, from 23°22′ S., 45°50′ W.)

100. Natural vegetation and culture patterns on the mature topography of the plateau about 36 miles east of São Paulo (NE, from 23°26′ S., 46°4′ W.)

101. Market gardens and orchards on the grasslands of the São Paulo basin, about 10 miles east of São Paulo

102. Looking across Santos and its harbor to the coastal escarpment bordering the Brazilian Plateau (NE)

103. The forested southern margin of the Brazilian Plateau, 65 miles west-southwest of the São Paulo airport (S, from ca. 24°4′ S., 47°34′ W.)

BRAZIL: SÃO PAULO TO IGUASSÚ FALLS*

São Paulo to Curitiba

THE course from São Paulo lay approximately S. 60°W. for the first
113 miles to 24°27′S., 48°15′W., where a definite control point was
secured, and thence approximately S. 40°W. to Curitiba. According to
the geologic map the entire region is underlain by Pre-Cambrian crystalline rocks. For the first 40 miles, topography and culture are essentially
the same as on the plateau east of São Paulo, except that the region
gradually becomes less settled and more forested westward. Fifty miles
from São Paulo all trace of human habitation disappears and the ground
is covered with a dense forest of large trees. The eastern end of Serra
Paranapiacaba rises considerably above the general level of the plateau,
but most of the land elsewhere is a maturely dissected plateau [103, 65
miles from São Paulo]. A tendency for the divides to be relatively flat
while the valleys are steep-sided and narrow, testifies to the active headward cutting of streams draining to the Atlantic. Rough land, with its
dense cover of untouched forest, continues for another 50 miles, but
about 10 miles south of the course for the last half of that distance, clearings were noted along the Rio Ribeira de Iguape.

About 12 miles beyond the point where the course was changed as
stated, we crossed the Rio Ribeira de Iguape. A view southeastward downstream [104] reveals only a limited primitive culture confined to the immediate vicinity of the stream. The fact that the river is flowing in a
narrowed portion of its course, marked on the map as being above even
canoe navigation from down the valley, undoubtedly accounts for the
low degree of culture along a stream that otherwise would have been a
useful highway.

The general character of the territory lying to the southeast of the
route for the preceding 80 miles is well illustrated by Figure 105, looking
southeast from about 50 miles northeast of Curitiba. Rugged, densely
forested mountains, in form reminiscent of those of New England, occupy most of the 40-mile-wide strip between our route and the coast.
To the northwest the land is almost equally rough.

A beautiful group of monadnock mountains [106] lies south of the

---

* See Map IV, p. 284, below.

course about 35 miles east-northeast of Curitiba. Another view of what is believed to be the same group of mountains [107] shows also the maturely dissected lower land surrounding them and bordering the Rio Pardo. The relief here is much more subdued than farther east. Scattered araucaria trees (Paraná pines) are recognizable in the foreground.

After passing a low divide on a continuation of the maturely dissected surface pictured here, we came over a broad smooth basin, grassy in its eastern part, in which, at an elevation of 3000 feet, lies the thriving city of Curitiba, the capital of Paraná.

Curitiba to the Iguassú Falls

From Curitiba to the Iguassú Falls, and thence to Asunción, the route lay almost due west: across the outcropping edges of a thick series of Paleozoic and Mesozoic sediments that constitute the eastern rim of a broad, shallow geological basin in the axis of which the Río Paraná flows; across the fields of ancient (probably Jurassic) lavas that cover the central part of the basin; and, finally, across disordered Paleozoic rocks on its western side, near Asunción. The more resistant of the sedimentary rocks on the eastern rim of the basin form a series of great north-south cuestas with steep escarpment slopes facing eastward. These divide the region into longitudinal belts of varying topography and soils, inducing corresponding variations in vegetation and human activities.

Curitiba, at the headwaters of the Rio Iguassú, lies on a gently rolling plain underlain by soft red sediments, probably of early Quaternary age. Far to the west, one sees from the ground a high, even-crested escarpment, stretching away to the north and south—the first of the great cuestas. But in the 20 miles between the city and the foot of the cuesta the ancient crystalline rocks, such as constitute the Brazilian highlands farther east, form a rolling terrain, rising gradually westward. This region is intensively cultivated and shows every indication of successful agriculture, apparently conducted by small landowners rather than on large fazendas.

Somewhat to the west of the better portion of this agricultural belt, Figure 108 (15 miles west of Curitiba) shows a typical landscape. Corn appeared to be the prinicipal crop. Here and farther west on the east-facing slope of the escarpment, much of the land is pasture. In the background is the trunk highway leading westward from Curitiba.

Twenty-five miles west of Curitiba, the edge of the cuesta is reached [109]. The cuesta is capped by a thick bed of resistant sandstone (lower Devonian) which outcrops as a cliff along its edge. Its summit, at an elevation of some 4000 feet, rises about 1000 feet above the Curitiba basin. The highway winding up the face of the escarpment is a continuation of that seen in the preceding picture.

The gently inclined back slope of the cuesta [110; 38 miles west of Curitiba] is an extensive grassy pasture of moderate relief, with brush along the bottoms of the shallow valleys and in irregular patches elsewhere. Bare rock outcrops in many places. Westward, as the sandstone dips beneath the surface [111; 49 miles west of Curitiba] the amount of brush increases in the valleys, and scattered farm houses appear, surrounded by a few acres of land devoted to crops, mainly corn.

Within the next 7 miles the quality of the soil has evidently improved, for we have reached an apparently prosperous agricultural region devoted mainly to general farming [112]. Farms appear to be well tilled and buildings well kept. Wood lots occupy a normal part of the total area. The tall trees with flat tops, appearing lighter than other trees in the forest, are Paraná pine. About 10 miles farther west a good deal of land formerly cultivated is being allowed to revert to brush.

Ten miles east of Iratí we pass from the Itararé formation of lower Permian glacial sediments and tillites, which weather into the rich agricultural land of the preceding picture, to a higher formation, the coal-bearing Tubarão series, which evidently does not produce soils suitable for agriculture [113]. Here, in spite of its proximity to a railroad and a considerable town (Iratí), the land is little cultivated. The slopes are in forest and brush, and the valley bottoms are grassy. Curiosity is aroused as to what prevents the growth of trees on the flood plains. A similar condition will be seen later in eastern Paraguay. A notable lumbering industry, utilizing the Paraná pine, was noted at Iratí.

Within 8 or 9 miles west of Iratí, we are again over rocks (Iratí group) which yield soils that permit cultivation [114]. The crop seemed to be mainly corn, but what was thought to be cotton was also noticed. The occurrence of many deadenings, where the forest was being cleared and new land brought under cultivation, at the same time that many of the fields appeared to be reverting to brush, suggested that the soils must become depleted so rapidly that a modified form of shifting culture has been adopted. This and preceding pictures reveal a rolling topography of moderate relief generally favorable for agriculture.

The second great cuesta along the route, Serra da Esperança [115; 30 miles west of Iratí and about 115 miles from Curitiba], rises 800 to 1000 feet above the rolling land at its eastern base. It is held up by the massive Botucatú sandstone, capped by thin beds of basalt[1] which represent the easternmost outcrops of the great Río Paraná lava fields. The eastern edge of the cuesta appears at the right center and top of the picture. Its crest and back slope remain largely forested.

On the forested back slope of the Serra da Esperança cuesta, about 12 miles east of Guarapuava, interesting openings were noted in the forest [116]. In the center of each of several small clearings is a house surrounded, about a hundred feet away, by a heavy wooden stockade. Though perhaps not visible on the regular-scale photograph, two of these should be recognizable on the small enlarged inset. According to James,[2] they are the transient homes of half-breed Indian and white migratory farmers known as *caboclos*, who erect the stockades to keep out the hogs that range in the corn planted in the surrounding woods. The forest here contains much Paraná pine (the large, fuzzy-appearing trees, especially numerous to the right of the center), which would seem to constitute an important timber resource.

Two miles west of Guarapuava (about 140 miles west of Curitiba), the forest gives way to an open grassland that extends far to the west and south on either side of the Rio Jordão. Figure 117, looking south-southeast from 18 miles S. 75°W. of Guarapuava, shows that river flowing in slightly entrenched meanders (over numerous rapids, however) through a rolling savanna. The forest, containing many araucaria, is confined to strips along the streams and to isolated patches elsewhere. A cattle ranch, similar to those seen at intervals on the savanna, appears in the left foreground. At the time of our flight (March 3) the region appeared to be suffering somewhat from drought, for the south sides of the hills were noticeably greener than the north.

---

[1] Personal communication from Glycon de Paiva; and A. I. de Oliveira and O. H. Leonardos: Geologia do Brasil, Rio de Janeiro, 1940.

[2] Personal communication from Preston E. James; and Preston E. James: The Expanding Settlements of Southern Brazil, *Geogr. Rev.*, Vol. 30, 1940, pp. 601–626.

According to the geologic map, the underlying rock here and all the rest of the way to Iguassú Falls is lava, belonging to the great series of volcanic flows and sills that covers about 300,000 square miles in the Paraná basin.[3]

Eleven miles farther on, the route left the grassland, which continued on to the southwest, and passed above a forest with occasional clearings. Figure 118, taken 40 miles still farther along the route, serves as a fair sample of the topography and culture crossed after the grassland was left behind. It shows primitive culture, apparently of the shifting type, that is probably a product of the devastating activity of the *caboclos*. A vague trail is recognizable, but there are no roads. Paraná pines are abundant in the forest.

For the next 50 miles, the Rio Iguassú—a winding, coffee-brown strip in a vivid green forest—lay 5 to 10 miles south of our route. Clearings decreased in number as we proceeded westward, and within 25 miles had disappeared entirely. From that point to Iguassú Falls (about 95 miles) not a trace of human activity was seen.

A good idea of the nature of the region may be had from Figure 119, looking southeast from about 68 miles above Iguassú Falls. The Rio Iguassú, a large stream, flows in broad meanders through a dense forest. Rapids noted at several points farther upstream indicate that the stream is beginning to entrench itself. The entrenchment has proceeded far enough so that no flood plain exists. However, a gorge has not yet been formed, and the late mature topography within the meander loops indicates that downcutting must be slow. A tributary stream meandering through the forest may be seen in the left foreground.

One of the larger of the rapids on the Rio Iguassú, Salto Faraday, about 48 miles above Iguassú Falls, is pictured in Figure 120. On either side of the river, as far as one can see both north and south, and forward all the way to Iguassú Falls, is the same gently swelling old-age topography with similar unbroken forest and a local relief that appeared to be not much if any more than 200 feet. In this region the Paraná pine was not observed.

Coming down for a landing at Iguassú the pilot circled the falls,

---

[3] Charles Laurence Baker: The Lava Field of the Paraná Basin, South America, *Journ. of Geol.*, Vol. 31, 1923, pp. 66–79.

giving his passengers a comprehensive but fleeting glimpse of one of the world's most beautiful cataracts [121–123]. The Rio Iguassú, with a volume ordinarily considerably less than that of Niagara, but swelling greatly in times of flood, spreads its waters over a wide expanse of island-studded rapids before spilling them in a broken curtain nearly 2 miles long into a gorge more than 200 feet below. The highest drop at Iguassú Falls is 230 feet—63 feet higher than Niagara.[4] In Figure 121 we are looking downstream at Gargauta do Diabo, near the center, and at the rapids on the left which supply the numerous cascades on the Argentine side. On either side of the gorge, near the top of the picture, may be seen the sites of two hotels, one in Argentina (left) and the other in Brazil. Figure 122, looking up the gorge, gives a glimpse obtainable only from the air, of the spray-drenched chasm into which the bulk of the water pours. It also displays clearly the mutual relations of river, rapids, falls, and the surrounding forest-covered lava plateau. The San Martín Falls, on the Argentine side [123], though carrying only a moderate share of the total volume of water, are among the most attractive because of their variety of form, their double cascade along part of the cliff, and their setting in a tropical forest, from which the water emerges to plunge directly into the gorge.

At the falls the Rio Iguassú drops into a narrow gorge which it has cut back 12 miles from its junction with the Río Paraná. That river also flows in a gorge [124] cut by the retreat of a waterfall similar to that of the Iguassú. During the time that has been required for the Iguassú Falls to retreat 12 miles, the falls of the much larger Paraná have retreated an air-line distance of 100 miles, to the present La Guayra Falls, or Salto das Sete Quedas.

[4] See Theodore W. Noyes: The World's Great Waterfalls, *Natl. Geogr. Mag.*, Vol. 50, 1926, pp. 29–59.

104. Mid-course of the Rio Ribeira de Iguape, the largest stream draining the seaward margin of the Brazilian Plateau in the some 700 miles between Rio de Janeiro and Pôrto Alegre (SE, from 24°33′ S., 48°22′ W.)

105. The dissected margin of the Brazilian Plateau 60 miles northeast of Curitiba (SE, from ca. 24°54′ S., 48°41′ W.)

106. An isolated group of mountains about 35 miles northeast of Curitiba (S, from ca. 25°0′ S., 48°46′ W.)

107. The headwaters of the Rio Pardo and a monadnock mountain mass, photographed from a point about 30 miles northeast of Curitiba (from ca. 25°7′ S., 48°52′ W.). Paraná pines in foreground

108. Rolling farm lands about 15 miles west of Curitiba (S, from 25°24′ S., 49°29′ W.)

109. The eastern edge of the great sandstone cuesta 25 miles west of Curitiba (S, from 25°24′ S., 49°40′ W.). The capping sandstone commonly forms a vertical cliff

110. Extensive grasslands on the back slope of the cuesta of Devonian sandstone (S, from 25°25′ S., 49°52′ W.)

111. A transition zone between the grasslands on the sandy soils of the cuesta and the forest farther west, 49 miles west of Curitiba (SSE, from 25°25′ S., 50°2′ W.)

112. Farm lands on a belt of favorable soils 56 miles west of Curitiba (SSE, from 25°25′ S., 50°9′ W.)

113. An area seemingly unsuited for agriculture, 76 miles west of Curitiba (SSE, from 25°25′ S., 50°28′ W.). The vegetational pattern is characterized by the presence of grasslands in the valley bottoms and brush forests on the uplands

114. Typical farm lands 95 miles west of Curitiba (S, from 25°25′ S., 50°46′ W.)

115. The eastern front of the lava-capped plateau of Serra da Esperança, 115 miles west of Curitiba and 23 miles east of Guarapuava (SSE, from 25°24′ S., 51°5′ W.)

116. Clearings and stockaded huts of *caboclos* on the forested back slope of the Serra da Esperança, 12 miles east of Guarapuava (S, from 25°24′ S., 51°15′ W.)

117. Natural grasslands utilized for cattle ranching, 18 miles west of Guarapuava (SE, from 25°28′ S., 51°44′ W.)

118. The "pioneer fringe" 69 miles west of Guarapuava (S, from 25°31′ S., 52°33′ W.)

119. The Rio Iguassú flowing in broad meanders through virgin forests, about 68 miles east of Iguassú Falls (SE, from 25°26′ S., 53°22′ W.)

120. Salto Faraday, one of the numerous rapids on the Rio Iguassú, about 48 miles east of Iguassú Falls (SSE, from 25°29′ S., 53°42′ W.)

121. Iguassú Falls from the southeast. The water drops about 230 feet into a chasm cut in basalt

122. Garganta do Diabo at Iguassú Falls (SE)

123. The San Martín cataracts on the Argentine side of Iguassú Falls

THE PARANA LOWLAND*

Iguassú Falls to Asunción

AFTER a few minutes on the ground in the moist and fragrant heat of a
jungle airport, we took off westward toward Asunción. Because of
the lack of adequate maps of Paraguay, no exact ground checks of location along the route could be secured. Consequently, the positions given
for the pictures are based mainly on timing between terminals and may as
a result be somewhat in error. For the first third of the course the route
lay between the Río Monday and the south branch of the Río Acaray.

From near the point where the Río Acaray joins the Paraná, a view to
the northeast [124] shows the Paraná in a steep-walled gorge, cut down
200 to 300 feet beneath the surface of the gently rolling plateau. The Río
Acaray, in the foreground, has not yet lowered itself noticeably into
the rock at the little village in the center, where it passes within a few
hundred feet of the Paraná gorge, but below that point it flows in
rapids all the way to its junction with the Río Paraná, a mile or two
to the right of the picture. An insignificant amount of excavation would
divert the stream directly into the Paraná, to create a power resource
that would be extremely valuable in a land less surfeited with potential
water power and better supplied with users. Small settlements and clearings appear close to the rivers, but most of the region is densely forested.

The geography of eastern Paraguay along the line of flight is epitomized in Figure 125, taken about 51 miles west of the Paraná. An old-age
topography of coarse texture and low relief is everywhere densely
forested except on the broad alluvial plains bordering the streams. These
are grass-covered and locally swampy, with the water showing through
a green scum of water hyacinths or similar plants. The streams wind
in intricate patterns across the alluvial plains in brush-covered meander
belts much narrower than the grassy flats. The light-green grasslands
assume a dendritic pattern visible for many miles in every direction in
contrast to the darker green of the forest. In the right foreground is the
first sign of human occupation seen since we left the Paraná. For another
30 miles, which brought us almost halfway across the country, we flew
over a similar landscape.

---

* See Maps IV and V, pp. 284 and 285, below.

Eighty to eighty-five miles west of the Paraná we passed an area of considerable settlement (similar to that in Figure 127), then a belt, 5 to 10 miles wide, of forest on a higher ground with a relief of 200 to 300 feet, before coming out into open country mainly covered with grass [126] about 106 miles west of the Paraná and 78 miles east of Asunción. This and the following two pictures were all taken in the broad divide region between the Paraná and the Paraguay rivers, where, evidently, the drainage is not well integrated and the climate is somewhat drier than farther east. Here the rain water, instead of forming through-flowing streams, loses itself on broad, swampy flats, the water of which disappears in the dry season.

The essential geographical conditions here, and for at least 15 miles to the west, seem to be similar to those in eastern Paraguay [125] except that the grassy alluvial flats cover most of the ground and the low, forested hammocks rise only here and there, like islands, between them.

A typical central Paraguayan landscape is pictured in Figure 127, about 72 miles east of Asunción. The land is sharply divided into the very gently rolling higher land, which is cultivated, and the grass-covered alluvial flats, which surround the higher ground like the sea on a drowned coast and are never cultivated. Aside from the trails, the latter are marked by curious mottlings in the soil. The Paraguayan cultural pattern is distinctive. It is characterized by small, irregular fields, trails being more common than roads, and a peculiar unkempt appearance of the fields caused, perhaps, by trees scattered at random over them.

Another view about 5 miles farther west [128] emphasizes some of the features of the preceding picture, especially the "drowned" character of the upland with respect to the alluvial flats, and the curious soil markings on the latter, which are similar in pattern to hammocks on a grassy delta or tidal swamp. Numerous white specks on the lighter portions of the flats are probably anthills, though possibly products of burrowing animals similar in habit to prairie dogs.

A clue to the reason why the flats are never cultivated was found at the Asunción airport, located on a similar flat. The ground was cracked and baked hard. Undoubtedly the flats are covered with water in the rainy season, and bake too hard for cultivation in the dry.

About 47 miles east of Asunción an area was crossed that is underlain by limestone (possibly Devonian) dipping about 20° in a southerly direction. For the next 20 miles, tilted and disturbed sedimentary rocks were noted, their more resistant members forming low ridges on an erosional plain of generally low relief. About 27 miles east of Asunción, this plain breaks down in a westward-facing, forested escarpment of perhaps 400 feet relief, to a grassy plain occupying a trough 5 to 10 miles wide extending approximately southeast.[1] About 20 miles to the south-southeast are flat-topped mesas breaking off westward into buttes [129]. These features are clearly revealed in the photograph, where the wooded escarpment extends from the center foreground directly away from the observer, the low grassy plain parallels the escarpment to the right, and the buttes and mesas appear in the distance.

Figure 130, looking south-southwest from about 18 miles east of Asunción, shows a typical landscape of this region. In the distance are rounded hills and low mesas. These are westward outliers of the ones previously mentioned, although some of them are presumably the volcanic plugs shown on the Denis map.

Details of culture in a typical Paraguayan landscape are represented in Figure 131, taken about 10 miles east-northeast of Asunción. Recognizable crops in Paraguay were corn, and possibly sugar cane and cotton, besides tree crops which appear to be especially important in the western part of the country. In this picture, perhaps a third of the land is devoted to such crops, although we could not determine from above whether they were citrus fruit or maté. The trees are low and stocky with glossy, dark-green leaves. A distinctive feature is the large number of tall palm trees (readily recognizable in the picture) scattered irregularly, but abundantly, everywhere through field and orchard. Their variety and use the writer has not been able to determine definitely, but the following quotations from Adams[2] suggest that they may be coconut palms: "Palms are a feature of the Paraguayan landscape. Oil is obtained from the nuts, which are also used in fattening stock. Hats, hammocks, ropes, and cloth are manufactured from a textile made from the leaves." And again, referring to an area east of Asunción not far from the point where

[1] This is probably the fault trough indicated by Denis in "Amérique du Sud" (Geographie Universelle, Vol. 15), Part 2, p. 449.

[2] Harriet Chalmers Adams: River-Encircled Paraguay, *Natl. Geogr. Mag.*, Vol. 63, 1933, pp. 385–416; references on pp. 410 and 396 respectively.

this picture was taken: "I was astonished to find the coconut palm so far from the sea."

The people evidently live on scattered small farms. Roads are mostly unimproved and not uncommonly detour around mudholes.

Asunción to Buenos Aires

From Asunción we flew southward to Buenos Aires. In Paraguay the route lay mainly over the alluvial plains east of the Río Paraguay, crossing the Río Paraná into Argentina near longitude 58° W., and thence across central Corrientes Province and eastern Entre Ríos to the western suburbs of Buenos Aires.

About 12 miles southeast of Asunción, Figure 132 shows the typical contact between the gently rolling upland, with intensively cultivated red soil, and the grassy alluvial flats at the right, the light mouse-colored soils of which are devoted exclusively to grazing. Tree crops are evidently important, and the general appearance of the landscape is distinctively Paraguayan—decidedly different from anything seen elsewhere in South America.

In western Paraguay the alluvium of the plains along the east side of the Río Paraguay, as well as that along smaller drainage lines from the interior, appears to be encroaching upon and drowning the higher ground in a manner similar to that observed in central Paraguay [127]. This condition is well illustrated on a broad scale by Figure 133, looking a little south of east from about 18 miles south-southeast of Asunción. The uncultivated alluvial plains occupy the left and middle distance, and the higher ground the right foreground. In the background are the same mesas and buttes seen in Figures 129 and 130. About 4 miles farther on we look northwest across the Río Paraguay [134]. On its flood plain are brush-grown meander scars, while in the foreground (probably along the top of a low bluff) are rounded patches of brush suggestive of sand hills. No cultivated land is visible.

Some 30 miles in a southerly direction from Asunción, and 10 miles east of the Río Paraguay, the grassy alluvial plains have widened considerably [135]. To the east, under the cloud, the cultivated higher ground may be seen dimly, while below, the dominant industry on the flats is betrayed by the presence of cattle trails and widely scattered corrals. Locally on the flats one sees lakes of considerable size. Some of these are rounded, though others, several miles in length, have a meander-like pattern suggesting that they may be remnants of an abandoned course of the Río Paraguay.

The Río Tebicuary, the principal stream of southern Paraguay, meanders in a most interesting fashion across the grassy plains [136]. Strips of light and dark soil, or meander tracks, mark successive stages of meander enlargement, and crooked oxbow lakes fill what are obviously old channels that were abandoned when the river made one of its numerous changes of course, and which were later silted up at the ends. For many miles on either side, and west to the Río Paraguay, the grassy plains continue, showing scarcely any signs of human occupation, though by careful search cattle trails and corrals may be found here and there. The plains are partly swampy during the dry season, but probably more or less completely flooded in the rainy season.

About 15 miles south of the Río Tebicuary a welcome change from the monotony of the almost featureless grasslands was offered by sandy areas fringed by groves of trees [137]. Lower grassy swales appeared to be remnants of former rounded ponds, now being obliterated by accumulating sediments and encroaching vegetation. The trees evidently afforded welcome shelter for the cattle, for in this area cattle trails are more numerous. About 5 miles farther south [138], many of the rounded ponds are still unfilled (black areas), while others show every stage of progressive extinction, in which advancing vegetation appears to be playing an important part. The concentric rings of varying shades no doubt represent different communities of vegetation pushing out into the water. The origin of such rounded ponds is an interesting problem, deserving of further study. Since they occur on an alluvial plain, it is suggested that they may be due to an uneven settling of the alluvium as it squeezes out some of the water and compacts under its own weight.

All of southern Paraguay, as far east as could be seen from 10,000 feet and west to the Río Paraguay, is a vast alluvial plain such as is revealed in the last four pictures. Cultivated land was noted only within a few miles of the Río Paraná—probably on its natural levee. The Paraná, flowing west at the border between Paraguay and Argentina, appears to be aggrading, for it occupies a very broad channel studded with large islands—a strong contrast to its condition near Iguassú Falls [124].

For about 70 miles south of the Río Paraná a severe thunderstorm prevented more than occasional glimpses of the ground. These showed that for at least 55 miles south of the river the land is similar to that of southern Paraguay, with numerous rounded ponds or small lakes in a grassy plain. However, in contrast to southern Paraguay, considerable cultivation was noted, especially of a tree crop (probably oranges).

Eighty to eighty-five miles south of the Río Paraná, in central Corrientes Province, the area of unorganized drainage and rounded ponds and swamps had been left behind. From there, south across Corrientes and Entre Ríos, the drainage is well organized into an open, symmetrical dendritic pattern of rather widely spaced streams and tributaries, though the relief is small and of a decidedly old-age type, as is shown in Figures 139, 140, and 141. In these pictures it may be noted that all of the streams are out of their banks in flood following the thunderstorm through which we had just passed. According to Buenos Aires papers the next morning, 100 millimeters (4 inches) of rain had fallen in this region during that storm.

These three pictures, distributed along 90 miles of the route, from 15 miles north-northeast of Mercedes to the vicinity of Monte Caseros on the Río Uruguay, are fairly representative of this great grazing region of central and southern Corrientes Province. All of the land is grass-covered, save occasional patches of low brush, and, with the exception of small plots near some of the ranch houses, none of it has been broken by the plow. A typical larger ranch establishment, or hacienda, is shown in Figure 139, north of Mercedes. Small streams have been dammed to supply water for stock, and trees have been planted as windbreaks around the ranch buildings, including the large barn at the left of the center. An interesting custom in this region is to plant triangular groves of trees—generally in fence corners—perhaps for wood or for cattle shelter. Figure 140, a few miles southeast of Mercedes, in which not a single road or hacienda is to be seen, emphasizes the large size of the landholdings and the sparsity of population. Figure 141, taken from about 20 miles southwest of Monte Caseros, shows similar ranch country, with a group of hacienda buildings, a road, and a wood lot in the foreground. In the background is the Río Uruguay. The entire region is fenced with wire. There are few roads and they are generally unpaved. On this wet afternoon they were lanes of water and deep mud, as could readily be seen even from a plane at 7000 feet.

From the site of Figure 141, the course for the next 80 miles was S. 20°W., generally parallel to the Río Uruguay and about 20 to 25 miles west of it. This region [142–145] is a transitional zone lying between the area of a dominant pastoral economy on the north and the grain-growing lands of southern Entre Ríos on the south. Figure 142, in decided contrast to preceding pictures, shows much of the land under cultivation, though considerable untilled areas may be seen in the left foreground and elsewhere. In the background is the Río Uruguay. The land has a low relief but evidently is well drained. The soil, as is true all the way across Entre Ríos and in Corrientes, is almost jet-black. Figures 143, 144, and 145, about 20 miles northwest and west of Concordia, show the breaking up of the pasture in varying degrees of completeness. Some large areas are almost untouched; others are divided into rectangles and almost entirely cultivated. No consistent pattern of land subdivision is used, however, as is the case in central and western United States.

No pictures are included for the next 140 miles to the north edge of the Río Paraná delta since the region is essentially the same as that shown in the three preceding photographs, except that, in general, it is more completely cultivated and has numerous towns, roads and railroads. Along the line of flight, the degree of agricultural development indicated on the preceding pictures continues unchanged to about the latitude of Gualeguaychú, where the soil assumes a brownish tint and becomes more sandy, and where more of the land is left in pasture. A short distance north of the Arroyo Ñancay, a belt of low sand hills marks the southern margin of the higher land and the northern edge of the great delta of the Paraná. The higher land appears to be drowned under the alluvium in much the same way as in Paraguay.

Nevertheless, a distinct belt of slightly elevated beaches [147] borders the estuary of the Río Uruguay and swings around westward toward the Paraná. The history of the recent relative movements of land and sea in this region is thus similar to that in the Vitória region of Brazil—a rela-

124. Looking across the gorge of the Río Paraná and the plains in which it is cut (NE, from 25°27′ S., 54°43′ W.). The Río Acaray in foreground

125. A typical view of the rolling plains in eastern Paraguay, 51 miles west of the Río Paraná (SE, from ca. 25°26′ S., 55°30′ W.). The land is everywhere forested except along the rivers

126. The grassy plains of central Paraguay, about 78 miles east of Asunción (S, from ca. 25°25′ S., 56°24′ W.)

127. Typical culture patterns in central Paraguay, 72 miles east of Asunción (S, from ca. 25°25′ S., 56°31′ W.).
      Rolling, cultivated uplands surrounded by grass-covered lowlands

128. Soil patterns on the grassy plains of central Paraguay (S, from ca. 25°25′ S., 56°36′ W.)

129. A view along a westward-facing escarpment to distant buttes and mesas, from a point 27 miles east of Asunción (S, from ca. 25°24′ S., 57°13′ W.)

130. A landscape typical of eastern Paraguay, 18 miles east of Asunción (S, from ca. 25°23′ S., 57°22′ W.)

131. Paraguayan croplands about 10 miles east-northeast of Asunción (SW, from 25°20′ S., 57°31′ W.)

132. Cultivated higher land bordering a grass-covered flood plain or terrace (right) along the Río Paraguay, 12 miles southeast of Asunción (E, from ca. 25°25′ S., 57°34′ W.)

133. Croplands (right foreground) bordered by grass-covered alluvial plains (left and middle distance), about 18 miles south-southeast of Asunción (E, from 25°34′ S., 57°35′ W.)

134. The Río Paraguay and its bordering plains, as seen from a point 28 miles south of Asunción (NW, from 25°40′ S., 57°36′ W.)

135. Broad, grassy plains east of the Río Paraguay, about 33 miles south of Asunción (E, from 25°45′ S., 57°36′ W.)

136. The Río Tebicuary meandering across the grassy plains of southern Paraguay
(ESE, from 26°26′ S., 57°43′ W.)

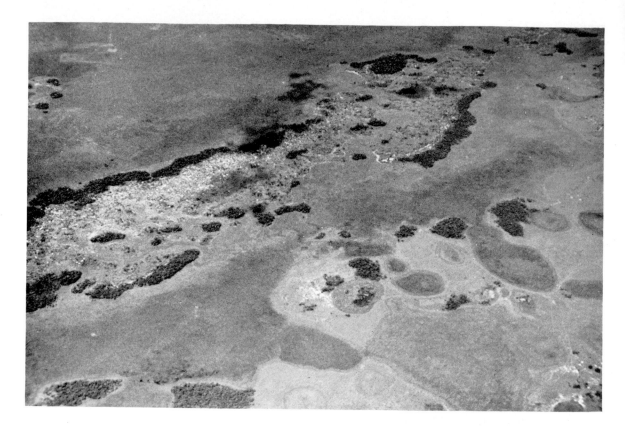

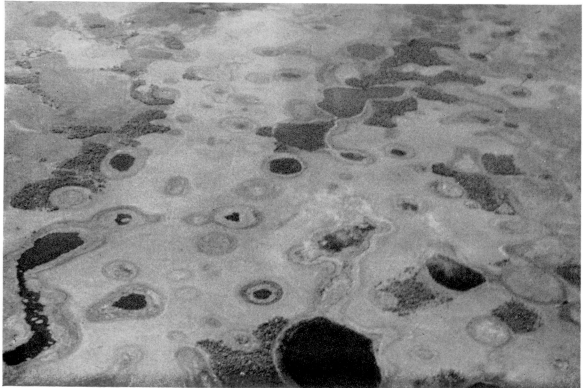

137. Sand hills and vegetation patterns on the alluvial plains of southern Paraguay, 15 miles south of the Río Tebicuary (E, from ca. 26°39′ S., 57°49′ W.)

138. Curious rounded ponds on the alluvial plains in all stages of obliteration by encroaching vegetation, 20 miles south of the Río Tebicuary (SE, from ca. 26°43′ S., 57°51′ W.)

139. A typical cattle ranch or hacienda on the plains of central Corrientes Province, Argentina, northeast of Mercedes (ESE, from ca. 28°53′ S., 58°3′ W.)

140. Typical grasslands of south-central Corrientes Province, southeast of Mercedes (E, from 29°13′ S., 58°2′ W.)

141. Unplowed grasslands of southern Corrientes, about 20 miles southwest of Monte Caseros (ESE, from 30°22′ S., 57°59′ W.). The Río Uruguay in background

142. Plains of northern Entre Ríos Province, about 50 miles north of Concordia (E, from 30°40′ S., 58°7′ W.). The rich black soils in this region are extensively cultivated

143. Pasture and plowed land about 20 miles northwest of Concordia (E, from 31°15′ S., 58°22′ W.)

144. Typical aspects of land development in north-central Entre Ríos, about 20 miles west of Concordia (E, from 31°23′ S., 58°26′ W.)

tively great subsidence, forming large estuaries, followed by a more recent slight relative rise of the land. In the photograph, a series of many brushy sand ridges, with intervening swales, parallels the Uruguay estuary, which appears in the upper third of the picture about 11 miles away at the nearest point. One may assume that the retreat of the sea was

145.   Grainlands about 20 miles west of Concordia (E, from 31°27′ S., 58°27′ W.)

more rapid in the later stages, since few evidences of beach ridges are to be seen for several miles inland from the estuary.

The northernmost distributaries of the Paraná delta begin about 45 miles south of Gualeguaychú, or about 70 miles north of the center of Buenos Aires. From there to a point about 6 miles northwest of Tigre on the bluff bordering the Río Paraná on the south—a distance of somewhat over 50 miles—the route lay over the delta, 10 to 18 miles west of the Uruguay estuary and far enough inland to be beyond the mud flats immediately bordering the estuary. The river divides into numerous distributaries as it crosses the delta, each of which is bordered by a natural levee of higher ground. These are formed during times of overflow, as the coarser sediment drops close to the stream in the slack water bordering the channel. The natural levees, therefore, are highest close to the

146. Croplands along the natural levee of one of the northern distributaries of the Río Paraná delta (E, from 33°48′ S., 58°43′ W.)

distributaries and slope gradually away from them to the low, swampy ground between. As a result they combine such favorable features as exceptionally fertile soils and reasonably good drainage. Adequate transportation is afforded by the distributaries themselves. These features, plus nearness to a large city and the vision necessary for a realization of the possibilities of the region—probably on the part of immigrants from sections of Europe where natural resources are intensively exploited— have made of the Paraná delta one great market garden and orchard, which can be seen and appreciated adequately only from the air.

On the more northerly distributaries [146; probably Arroyo Brazo Largo] culture is confined to the natural levees in a belt gradually narrowing downstream. Considerable land remains unreclaimed between distributaries. All houses are situated on the banks of the stream. Where distributaries are relatively close together they are joined by canals, such as that seen above the center of the picture, permitting easy travel from one to another. Winding traces across the plain mark former distributary courses.

In Figure 148, the restriction of cultivation to a strip along the natural levee is clearly shown. Evidently most of the ground is used for tree nurseries. Fields are commonly divided into compartments by hedges of tall Lombardy poplars, as at the right of the cultivated area. A portion of the delta that is almost entirely reclaimed [149] lies about 10 miles north-northwest of Tigre, south of the southern large distributary, visible in the background of the picture.

Two or three miles farther on, along the Río Luján distributary, details of typical culture are shown from a relatively low elevation [150]. Most of the land is occupied by orchards, but some, as at the lower right, is planted to densely growing woods. The distribution of houses (and probably also packing sheds) along the banks of the stream is typical, as are the hedges of Lombardy poplar. The appearance of this region from the ground, in a section devoted mainly to market gardening near San Isidro, is shown in Figure 151.

From far to the north over the delta, a white patch had appeared in the southeast that grew gradually larger, finally resolving itself into a recognizable city—Buenos Aires. In an almost smoke-free air, the city was amazingly white as it reflected the afternoon sun.

147. Elevated beaches bordering estuary of the Río Uruguay, about 80 miles north of Buenos Aires (NE, from 33°36′ S., 58°44′ W.)

148. A portion of the Río Paraná delta where cultivation is confined to the lands bordering the distributaries (E, from 34°1′ S., 58°42′ W.)

149. Orchards and market gardens on the delta of the Río Paraná, about 22 miles north-northwest of Buenos Aires (ENE, from 34°19′ S., 58°41′ W.)

150. A detailed view of the croplands (mostly orchard) on the Paraná delta near Tigre, 20 miles northwest of Buenos Aires (E, from 34°22′ S., 58°40′ W.)

151. Market gardens of the Paraná delta, as seen from the ground near San Isidro, a northwestern suburb of Buenos Aires

152. Cemetery on the outskirts of Buenos Aires

153-156.   (See opposite page)

BUENOS AIRES TO SANTIAGO*

Buenos Aires to Córdoba

THE air-line route from Buenos Aires northwest about 400 miles to Córdoba traverses one of the best parts of the famous Argentine Pampa,[1] where rainfall, though somewhat undependable, is adequate for the growing of corn, wheat, flax, alfalfa, and similar crops. The pictures which follow may be taken, therefore, as representative of the grain-growing region of the country. Similar conditions would be found on a journey either west or southwest from Buenos Aires, except that in those directions the dry belt, perforce devoted to grazing, would be reached somewhat more quickly.

About half a minute after the take-off from the airport on the western outskirts of Buenos Aires, we passed over a miniature city [152], the architecture of which shows that in South America reference to a cemetery as a "city of the dead" is not entirely a figure of speech.

Some 35 miles from Buenos Aires, and 10 miles N. 33°E. from Luján, Figure 157 shows a typical landscape. The land is flat and generally unmodified by erosion, although the larger streams (such as the Río Luján, crossed a few moments before) have entrenched themselves slightly, and their tributaries are beginning to cut shallow troughs in the plain, like the one crossing the center of the picture. A railroad (lower left to upper right), well graded roads, and scattered farm homes, generally surrounded by a windbreak of trees, constitute a cultural landscape very similar to that of central United States and, except for the adjoining province of Entre Ríos, strikingly different from anything previously seen along our route in South America. The greater part of the land in

---

* See Map V, p. 285, below.
[1] See Mark Jefferson: Peopling the Argentine Pampa, *Amer. Geogr. Soc. Research Series* No. 16, New York, 1926.

TITLES TO FIGURES 153–156.
153. The Andes rise as an imposing wall beyond the vineyards of the Mendoza region, 12 miles south of Mendoza (W, from 33°4′ S., 68°53′ W.). See pages 138 and 139
154. A ground view of the Pampa about 5 miles east of Luján
155. Summer homes in the Córdoba hills, as seen from a point west of Lago San Roque (SSW). Western front of the southern continuation of the Sierra Chica in the background. See pages 135 and 136
156. Stereoscopic view of tall cumulus clouds typical of tropical latitudes (NW, from 11°22′ S., 37°15′ W.). See page 45

this region is utilized as pasture. Corn appeared to rank second in areal importance, followed by wheat, and perhaps also flax.

The typical aspect of this region as seen from the ground is pictured in Figure 154, taken along the railroad between Buenos Aires and Luján. Cattle in large numbers graze on the plain, and windmills are common features in the landscape. Barns are small or entirely lacking since the hay is kept in stacks. The plain is treeless except for windbreaks planted near the buildings. Another view of the Pampa [158], about 75 miles northwest of Buenos Aires, shows a smooth plain devoted about equally to pasture and to grain. In the center is a typical small railroad town (Duggan), and in the left background what is probably a large cattle hacienda. The identity of the latter is suggested by the large contiguous area devoted to pasture, the groves of trees in distinctive patterns, and the lack of scattered farm homes.

Less than 20 miles beyond, we came over the edge of a solid mass of stratus clouds that, lying at an elevation of three or four thousand feet, obscured the ground for the next 80 miles. Arranged in rows, the scattered, small cumulo-stratus clouds first encountered graded into continuous windrows of similar clouds parallel to the front of the cloud bank and separated from one another by clear air. Finally we passed above the unbroken overcast [159]. Over the entire area, the top of the clouds was marked by an interesting compound wave pattern consisting of major waves parallel to the windrows along the front, flatly convex on the top and so thin in the narrow troughs as to permit occasional glimpses of the ground, and a set of much smaller, billowy waves lying nearly at right angles to the larger ones. Timing indicated that the waves of the larger set measured a mile to a mile and a half from trough to trough. I believe that they lay at right angles to the wind direction within the cloud mass. The smaller ones may possibly have had a similar relation to a cross wind above the cloud bank. An offsetting and suturing of the larger waves is visible near the center of the picture.

Forty-five miles southwest of Rosario the far edge of the cloud bank was crossed [160]. Like the other margin, it was broken into windrows of alternating cloud and clear air parallel to, and of essentially the same dimensions as, the larger wave patterns of the main cloud bank. Through the openings, the ground could be seen to be much more intensively cultivated than it had been between Buenos Aires and the point 80 miles back, where we had last seen it.

Thirty-nine miles farther on (65 miles west and 10 miles south of Rosario), Figure 161 revals a flat, cultivated plain, apparently divided into moderate-sized farms, each with its farm home. A typical farmstead consists of house, barn, orchard, and various outbuildings. The principal crops are wheat and corn. Some of the land is devoted to pasture. In this entire region the soil where freshly plowed has a pinkish-gray color and appears to be very rich.

The physiographic youth of the region is indicated by the fact that not a trace of a drainage course is to be seen, in spite of an elevation of some 300 feet above sea level and a drop of almost that amount within 60 miles along a through stream that passes not 5 miles away and flows directly into the Río Paraná.

Five miles farther on, from a point over the Río Carcaraña, a view southwestward up one of its tributaries [162] shows the characteristic immaturity of the landscape. The two lakes seem to lie in low places in the shallow bed of a watercourse. Like several others noted in the region, this watercourse is obviously not a product of erosion after the region was raised above sea level but, rather, seems to represent an old tidal inlet. Through such inlets streams from the higher land farther west used to find their way across the swampy flats that in comparatively recent geologic time were uplifted to become the Pampa.

A group of buildings surrounded by tall windbreak hedges, below and to the right of the center [162], no doubt marks one of the larger haciendas. Groves of planted trees in the near-by fields, as well as a group of buildings much larger than that associated with the typical farm home in this region, indicate a landholding of greater than average size.

Forty-seven miles farther on (108 miles west and 16 miles north of Rosario), an especially fine picture was obtained [163] of peculiar linear markings which in this region cross the plains in various directions. These are entirely independent of present field boundaries and intersect each other in "knots" such as that shown in the foreground. Measurements made on the photograph indicate that the larger "trails" are about 100 feet wide and that the "knot" in the foreground is about 300 feet in diameter. A comparison with the groups of farm buildings demonstrates that these figures cannot be far wrong. The centers of the "trails" are a lighter color than the average for the plain and support poorer crops, although a band on either side is decidedly darker and more fertile than the average, as was indicated by much greener and taller crops. A careful check at the time led to the tentative conclusion that the markings were animal trails dating from a period prior to the fencing and plowing of the region. Dr. Alfredo Castellanos, director of the Instituto de Fisografía y Geología of Rosario, believes that the "trails" were made, before the land was plowed, by cattle coming to water holes, or *jagüeles*, which the inhabitants had formed by excavating shallow concave basins and lining them with loess or clay so as to catch and hold the rain water.[2]

About 12 miles farther on we passed Bell Ville, one of the larger towns along the route [164]. Situated on the Río Tercero, a through-flowing stream from the Córdoba hills, it is arranged symmetrically around a central plaza and is a center from which roads radiate to the surrounding country. In the right foreground is one of the railroads connecting Rosario with Córdoba.

The topography of this region is similar to that observed to the southeast. A short distance away from the stream no drainage lines appear, but vague markings and occasional fairly distinct channels indicate watercourses that were occupied before the land was raised to its present elevation.

Beyond Bell Ville the natural vegetation—much of it consisting of low brush—indicates a climate considerably drier than farther to the southeast. In a belt about 10 miles wide, beginning about 40 miles beyond Bell Ville, light mottled areas still uncleared of brush suggest the presence of low sand hills or areas where the soil is too sandy for cultivation, and many formerly cultivated areas have the appearance of having been abandoned, at least temporarily. As is shown in Figure 165, a picture taken from a position 55 miles beyond Bell Ville, 65 miles southeast of Córdoba and about 8 miles northeast of Chañares (the village appearing near the upper center of the picture), the soil beyond that belt is less sandy and more widely cultivated. The average elevation in this region is about 800 feet.

A typical landscape about 35 miles southeast of Córdoba [166] shows a

---

[2] A statement made in response to a letter of inquiry enclosing one of these photographs.

flat plain, similar to the preceding, devoted almost entirely to wheat, with perhaps an occasional field of flax and certainly some alfalfa. Some of the fields, such as that in the lower left-hand corner, seem to be temporarily abandoned and growing up to weeds and brush, but the ragged checkered pattern common here and on some of the preceding pictures proved, with later inspection on the ground, to be made by dark-green weeds growing in the fields after the wheat had been cut and before the fall plowing had begun. In some of the fields a smooth, even tone indicates that plowing has been started (March 25).

Looking steeply down on the Río Segundo as we crossed it 22 miles southeast of Córdoba, we see an interesting pattern in sand beneath the water [167]. The river is flowing from the top of the picture to the bottom. At the top center is some of the native vegetation—containing a larger admixture of brush than the average, perhaps because of its close proximity to the river.

Córdoba is situated on the plain about 10 miles from the eastern edge of the Córdoba hills, a north-south fault-block mountain mass of granites, gneisses, and schists, reaching elevations which in places exceed 8000 feet. The city is a trading center for the surrounding country and the seat of the second oldest university in South America. Its early settlement and much of its present prosperity were, and are, based on the extensive irrigation made possible by water from the near-by mountains.

The Córdoba hills, because of their ready accessibility from the populous centers on the plains to the east and southeast—Santa Fé, Rosario, and Buenos Aires—and also because of their agreeable verdure as compared with the much drier Andes farther west, are a popular summer resort. Many beautiful summer homes dot the accessible parts of the mountains, particularly in that portion of the Valle de la Punilla from Lago San Roque, a large storage reservoir for power and irrigation, to La Cumbre. Typical examples of such homes are shown in Figure 155. The photograph also shows the prominent westward-facing fault scarp or fault-line scarp extending both northward and southwestward from Lago San Roque and forming the straight eastern border of Valle de la Punilla.[3]

---

[3] For a geological report and map of this region see Franco Pastore: Hoja 20¹ del mapa geológico de la Argentina: Región oriental media de la sierra de Córdoba, *República Argentina, Minist. de Agric., Dirección de Minas y Geol., Bol. No. 36, 1932.*

Córdoba to Mendoza

On the flight from Córdoba to Mendoza, clouds prevented any comprehensive view of the Córdoba hills (Sierras de Córdoba) and permitted only a glimpse, near the summit, of a flat surface of granite covered in patches by a sparse growth of grass and low shrubs. The appearance of the range as a whole, in the latitude of Córdoba, is suggestive of the presence of three eastward-tilted fault blocks of crystalline rocks, each having abrupt escarpments facing west and relatively gentle dip slopes to the east. The eastern block, Sierra Chica, the western face of which is shown in Figure 155, is composed of schist, while the central and highest mass is mainly granite.

West of the Sierras de Córdoba is a great semiarid, brush-covered plain devoted to ranching, the monotonous uniformity of which is epitomized by Figure 168, looking northeastward from a point about 20 miles west of the hills. Scattered ranch homes (light areas) are connected by roads laid out on a generally rectangular pattern. On parts of the plain (not visible in this picture) cultivation has been attempted, but the plowed areas are small and many of them appear to have been abandoned.

Rising out of the plain about 55 miles beyond the western border of the Sierras de Córdoba is a long, nearly straight, eastward-facing escarpment of what would seem to be another tilted fault block, the Sierra de Ulapes [169]. The scarp, about 13 miles from the camera in the center of the picture, trends a little west of north. In Figure 170 one is looking down to the north near the southern end of the escarpment. The rocks exposed in the face of the scarp appear to be either igneous or metamorphic and show a pronounced sheeting, dipping steeply westward. In the foreground is a ranch establishment with several ponds reflecting the noonday sun. The semiarid climate is clearly revealed by the sparse xerophytic vegetation.

Looking north along the top of the upland block, Figure 171 shows its remarkably even, gently curved eastern front and the more or less rectangular fracture patterns characteristic of igneous and metamorphic rocks. These guide the drainage of the upland. Two or three miles west of the front and parallel to it is a contact between light and dark rock (also apparent in Figure 169) that offers a puzzle to those interested in interpreting geology from aerial photographs. It may be due to a fault or to an intrusion of light rock into dark, but seems too smoothly curved and too closely parallel with the front for either. The generally smooth surface of the block indicates that, before the suggested faulting, these crystalline rocks had been worn down to a nearly plane surface (peneplain). The relatively small amount of headward erosion along the steep scarp front would seem to betray the comparative recency of faulting.

West of the Sierra de Ulapes lies the Pampa de la Salina, an undrained basin occupied by a partly dried-up salt lake. A view southeastward across the southern end of this lake [172] shows shallow water and salt flats in the foreground and beyond a semiarid brushy plain, similar to those seen in preceding pictures.

Thirty miles beyond the western edge of the Pampa de la Salina we passed over the center of a large anticline [173], trending north-south or a little west of north. This structure brings to the surface a belt about 6 miles wide of bluish-gray clays or clay shales (to judge by the fine-textured dendritic pattern of the topography), bordered on each side by a belt of red beds about 4 miles wide on the east and 7 on the west.

About 30 miles to the left of our course, in the approximate trend of this anticline, is a conspicuous dome surrounded by inward-facing escarpments. The anticline is probably the Sierra de Guayaguas, and the dome at the south the Sierra de las Ouijadas. All of these faulted and folded structures, from the Sierras de Córdoba westward, are related to the broad part of the Andean highland to the north and northwest in such a way as to suggest that they are a southward-fading expression of the crustal movements which formed that highland.

The Río Desaguadero, true to its name in having no apparent water, was crossed at about latitude 32° 19′ S. Ten miles west of the river a ranker growth of brush was encountered, and a few corrals were noted. Within an additional 10 miles we found ourselves over a monotonous plain covered by a dull-gray material that looked like gravel. No drainage lines or specific vegetation patterns were visible on this surface, but within a very few miles a conspicuous wind-controlled design appeared [174] and continued with a consistent north-northwest trend for 25 or 30 miles to the outer margins of the irrigated area east of Mendoza. The pattern suggests the presence of low sand hills, covered by a sparse growth of low brush. No evidences of human activity were seen throughout the region. With few roads and to all appearances uninhabited, the entire area from here east to the Sierra de Ulapes is comparatively inaccessible.

About 35 miles east-northeast of Mendoza we entered the area irrigated by water from the Andes. Here a great piedmont alluvial plain has been reclaimed and utilized mainly for the culture of grapes and other fruit, but also for a general type of agriculture in which alfalfa has a prominent place. A typical view in the Mendoza region is afforded by Figure 153. From a point 12 miles south of Mendoza we are looking across the vineyards and the windbreaks of Lombardy poplar to the great wall of the Andes, which everywhere dominates the landscape. Seen from the foothills near Potrerillos [175], this impressive mountain barrier rising abruptly to 18,000 feet is a spectacle not soon to be forgotten. In the foreground is the scattered xerophytic vegetation characteristic of the lower mountain slopes.

Mendoza to Santiago

The flight across the Andes from Mendoza at their eastern base in Argentina to Santiago similarly situated on their western side in Chile required only 66 minutes, but to one making the crossing for the first time those minutes are full and exhilarating. Taking off to the south from the Mendoza airport, we turned westward over the city to make a short cut across the front range into the valley of the Río Mendoza. We reached the valley a short distance below Uspallata and followed it to the pass, utilized by the railroad and highway, at La Cumbre, thence down the valley of the Río Aconcagua to the western border of the higher mountains, where we turned south to Santiago. We crossed the pass at 14,000 feet, about 1400 feet above the statue "Christ of the Andes," but well below the higher mountains on both sides.

The Mendoza region is too dry for agriculture without irrigation, but the Río Mendoza, fed by the snows of the high Andes, supplies water that has converted a large portion of the piedmont alluvial slope into a veritable garden. This is strikingly shown in Figure 176, looking southeast from over the outskirts of the city. Except for the orchards, easily recognizable in the foreground, most of the cultivated area is devoted to grapes. This view from the air gives some idea of the vast extent of the vineyards seen from the ground in Figure 153.

Looking north from a point about 8 miles west-southwest of Mendoza [177], we find the mountains projecting out into the plains in long spurs, seemingly half buried in the gravels of a great piedmont alluvial fan. The spurs mark transverse faults interrupting the continuity of the dominant eastward thrust faults which characterize the eastern front of the Andes in this region. To the left of the center, Mesozoic rocks dipping steeply to the left have been thrust up over late Tertiary gravels. The mountain spurs behind are composed of older and more resistant rocks upraised by the transverse faulting.

Above the front range, and looking toward the south [178], we see on the distant plains, about halfway between the center and the right margin of the picture, a broad swell on which is located one of Argentina's newest and richest oil fields. This, the Tupungato field, is associated with a structure that appears to be a continuation of the southward-pitching southern end of the front range (the Sierra de los Paramillos). As it plunges southward, the range detaches itself *en échelon* from the main Andean mass to the north, and is separated from it to the south by a wide basin of more or less crumpled Mesozoic and Tertiary rocks extending from near Potrerillos to Tupungato. The low rainfall of the region is betrayed by the sparse vegetation on the mountains in the foreground.

On the divide (15 miles west of Mendoza) between the steep eastern slope of the front range and the above-mentioned basin, here crossed by the Río Mendoza, a large remnant of old-age topography of low relief testifies to the physiographic recency of the mountain uplift [179]. The old-age upland is being attacked by erosion from all sides. The stream draining the valley on the divide is beginning to entrench itself where it tumbles over the edge in the center foreground, but it seems destined to lose most of its water by capture when the cliff to the right of the center will have retreated westward a few hundred feet farther.

From over the Río Mendoza, about 4 miles below the station of Uspallata, a view to the south-southwest [180] shows something of the barrenness and geological complexity of the eastern Andes. On the sky line are the peaks of the Nevado de la Plata, which, reaching a height of 18,000 feet, form one of the four high mountain masses in this part of the Andes. These are the mountains seen in the background in Figure 175.

From above a point one or two miles west of the Uspallata station, a view to the north-northeast [181] is surprising to one who has previously seen only the abrupt eastern front of the mountains, as shown in Figures 153, and 175. Instead of rugged mountains, one finds an old-age, pedimented desert landscape stretching beyond the limits of vision to the north and, apparently, nearly to the edge of the front range on the northeast. Beyond the mountains, at the right of the picture, may be seen the even sky line of the great plains of Argentina. The Uspallata basin, situated at an elevation of 6000 to 8000 feet, is the southernmost representative of the old-age *puna* topography characteristic of the Andean plateau farther north in Argentina and Bolivia. Toward the south, such topography ends abruptly at the Río Mendoza. A portion of the Uspallata basin has been irrigated, but most of it is a gravelly waste.

A view forward over the wing, from about 3 miles beyond Uspallata [183], is looking up the valley of the Río Mendoza (center), which, with the Transandine Railway and highway, we turned to follow southwestward. On the center sky line are the high peaks of the Nevado del Plomo, one of the four groups of high, snow-covered mountains that rise well above the general summit level in this part of the Andes. The others are the Nevado de la Plata, already seen, the Aconcagua group, and the huge volcano, Tupungato. About halfway between the center of the picture and its left-hand margin is the straight edge of a remarkably smooth and comparatively flat old-age surface remnant similar to those of the Uspallata basin, though several thousand feet above them (near the Zanjon Amarillo station). The surface bevels smoothly across red granite (or gneiss) and appears to have an extent of somewhat more than a square mile. It indicates that the mountain block south of the Río Mendoza, like that north and east of Uspallata, was reduced to old age before suffering, apparently, a much greater uplift and dissection than those that have affected the Uspallata basin.

A view northward over the west side of the Uspallata basin [182], shows the strong topographic contrast between the mountains west of the basin and those in and east of it [181]. This condition of topographic youth to the west and old age to the east suggests a relatively recent uplift

157. Pasturelands on the Pampa about 35 miles northwest of Buenos Aires (SSW, from 34°27′ S., 59°2′ W.)

158. A pastoral landscape about 75 miles west-northwest of Buenos Aires (S, from 34°11′ S., 59°39′ W.)

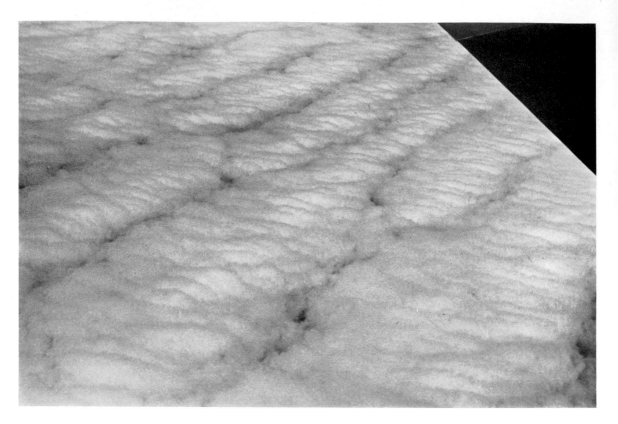

159. Cloud wave patterns (WSW, from 33°45′ S., 60°32′ W.)

160. Cloud windrows at the western edge of a cloud bank, 45 miles southwest of Rosario (SW, from 33°24′ S., 61°12′ W.)

161. Farm lands and homes on the flat plain 65 miles west-southwest of Rosario (from 33°6′ S., 61°46′ W.). Vague trail-like markings may be seen crossing the fields

162. Shallow lakes in what appears to be an ancient river channel, about 70 miles west of Rosario, surrounded by culture patterns typical of this part of the Pampa (SW, from 33°3′ S., 61°50′ W.)

163. Curious trail-like patterns, presumably made by animals before the land was plowed, on the Pampa 110 miles west-northwest of Rosario (SW, from 32°41′ S., 62°30′ W.)

164. Bell Ville, a small city on the Pampa (SW, from 32°35′ S., 62°40′ W.)

165. A typical landscape about 65 miles southeast of Córdoba (SW, from 32°5′ S., 63°24′ W.)

166. Harvested wheat lands, 35 miles southeast of Córdoba (SW, from 31°47′ S., 63°49′ W.)

167. Sand patterns beneath the waters of the Río Segundo, 22 miles southeast of Córdoba (SW, from 31°38′ S., 63°56′ W.)

168. Ranching on the brushy plains west of the Sierras de Córdoba (NNE, from ca. 31°46′ S., 65°38′ W.)

169. The straight east-facing scarp of the Sierra de Ulapes, as seen from a point about 115 miles south-west of Córdoba (WNW, from 31°54′ S., 66°4′ W.)

170. A view near the southern end of the Sierra de Ulapes (N, from 31°57′ S., 66°15′ W.)

171. The upland summit of the Sierra de Ulapes, apparently a westward-tilted fault block of crystalline rocks (N, from 31°58′ S., 66°16′ W.)

172. The southern end of Pampa de la Salina, one of the numerous saline playas of western Argentina (ESE, from 32°7′ S., 66°47′ W.)

173. Mature topography in miniature on the crest of the Sierra Guayaguas anticline, about 103 miles northeast of Mendoza (N, from ca. 32°15′ S., 67°16′ W.)

174. Wind-formed patterns and scattered brush vegetation on plains west of the Río Desaguadero, 55 miles northeast of Mendoza (S, from 32°31′ S., 68°0′ W.)

175. High Andes of the Nevado de la Plata group, as seen from the foothills near Potrerillos (WSW, from 32°58′ S., 69°13′ W.)

176. Irrigated vineyards and orchards near the southeastern outskirts of Mendoza (SE, from 32°54′ S., 68°49′ W.)

177. Outlying spurs and gravel-covered plains at the eastern base of the Andes, as seen from a position about 8 miles west-southwest of Mendoza (N, from 32°56′ S., 68°57′ W.)

178. The eastern front of the Andes, 13 miles west of Mendoza (S, from 32°54′ S., 69°4′ W.)

179. A remnant of old-age topography on the summit of the Andes front range, 15 miles west of Mendoza (N, from 32°54′ S., 69°5′ W.)

180. The Nevado de la Plata, one of the higher mountain groups in the Andes (SSW, from 32°44′ S., 69°19′ W.)

181. The Uspallata basin, a southern representative of the old-age *puna* topography common farther north (NNE, from 32°41′ S., 69°24′ W.)

182. The western side of the Uspallata basin, with the Río Mendoza in the foreground (NNE, from 32°42′ S., 69°30′ W.)

183–186.   (See opposite page)

and dissection of the western area, as was inferred in connection with the flat upland remnant described in the preceding paragraphs.

As the plane turned southwest up the Río Mendoza valley the giant peak of Aconcagua came into view 30 miles to the west [187]. Rising to 22,835 feet, Aconcagua, the highest peak in the western hemisphere, towers far above any of the surrounding mountains. Its form suggests a volcanic origin, but geological investigation has shown that in reality it is a monadnock remnant left standing high while surrounding rocks were worn away.

From a position opposite the often-described Cerro de los Penitentes, a view toward the south [188] shows a portion of the high Andes composed of steeply tilted and strongly eroded sedimentary rocks. On the sky line, partly under a cloud near the left-hand margin of the picture, is Cerro Tupungato, an extinct or quiescent volcano only about 1300 feet lower than Aconcagua. A portion of the Penitentes appears in the lower left corner of the photograph. They are giant semi-detached pillars formed by the erosion of weak, flat-bedded rocks, which from above look like volcanic ash or tuff.

Black and white pictures cannot adequately portray the beauty of a flight over the Andes because of the importance of color. Though on the whole not so brilliant as those of the Grand Canyon of the Colorado River in Arizona, colors in the Andes are surprisingly vivid. Granites of all shades from light pink to deep red, volcanic ash beds and tuffs of yellow or brownish orange, light-blue limestones, deep reddish-purple lavas, and rusty metamorphic rocks combine to weave a complex and interesting color pattern.

Because of the extreme ruggedness of the high Andes, as well as the fractured condition of many of the rocks, enormous masses of talus partly choke the mountain valleys and cirques. In Figure 189, on the south side of the valley about 2½ miles above Puente del Inca, we looked

TITLES TO FIGURES 183–186.

183. Looking up the valley of the Río Mendoza to the Nevado del Plomo in the background (SW, from 32°40′ S., 69°26′ W.)

184. A view toward the ocean, 40 miles away, from a point about 29 miles southeast of Illapel (NW, from 31°58′ S., 70°53′ W.). See page 165

185. An old-age upland 50 miles north of Taltal, which drops off in a 6000-foot cliff to the sea (NE, from 24°42′ S., 70°33′ W.). See page 182

186. A stereoscopic view of the western front of the Andes, 29 miles north of Santiago (ESE, from 33°1′ S., 70°46′ W.). The Nevado del Plomo rises on the sky line. See page 164

down into a steep-walled valley head partly filled with such a mass of broken rock fragments. Of particular interest in this picture are the several craters of various sizes in the talus. Perhaps remnants of a waning glacier lie buried beneath the talus and the craters have formed where water falling to the floor of the glacier melts out vertical wells or moulins into which the loose rock slides. About a mile and a half farther on [190] the camera recorded what appeared to be a slowly flowing mass of talus in a valley head, though the presence of glacial ice beneath a veneer of talus is strongly suspected. Interesting flow patterns may be seen on the surface, especially at the foot of the great talus slide at the left. The Andes bear unmistakable evidence of the former presence of powerful glaciers, compared with which those still existing are but dwindling remnants. Among the indications that they once extended far below their present levels are the straight-walled U-shaped valleys, such as that shown in the center of Figure 191 (believed to be that of the Río Blanco) about 15 miles beyond the pass on the Chilean side.

As we were gliding rapidly down to lower altitudes, a typical view of the west face of the Andes was obtained [192], looking south from a point about 11 miles southeast of Los Andes. The complexity of the rock structure is evident. In this part of the Andes great thicknesses of lava flows and associated agglomerates compose much of the front. In the distance, below the sky line, are some of these lavas showing either cross-bedding on a gigantic scale or, possibly, peculiar over-thrusting that does not involve the beds beneath.

About 18 miles south of Los Andes, at the foot of the higher mountains, we passed the first cultivated fields, surrounded by fences of brush [193]. The native vegetation in this view is the largest and thickest seen anywhere on the Andean crossing. Nowhere in this latitude do the Andes support anything even remotely resembling a forest.

As we approached Santiago the mountains were left behind and we passed over the irrigated fields of the Vale of Chile [194]. In this picture, from a point about 6 miles northwest of the center of Santiago, we are looking a little north of east toward the Nevado del Plomo on the sky line. A mile or so farther on a glimpse steeply down [195] reveals in greater detail the character of the farms and orchards close to the city. Here, as in the Mendoza region, grape culture (upper left) and orcharding are prominent. From above the western edge of Santiago [196] we looked down upon the busy capital of Chile, situated on a broad, sloping alluvial plain at the foot of the mountains. Above the plain rise isolated rocky hills such as Santa Lucía (the dark patch on the far side of the larger city buildings) and Cerro San Cristóbal (the higher hill to the left), both of them, apparently, volcanic plugs. Far behind, among the clouds, are the snow-clad peaks of the Nevado del Plomo.

As the plane touched ground a few miles south of Santiago, 163 miles by flight course from Mendoza, one of the world's most formidable mountain barriers had been crossed in 66 all too brief minutes.

187. Aconcagua, 22,835 feet, towers high above the Andean sky line (W, from 32°43′ S., 69°32′ W.)

188. Steeply dipping sedimentary rocks on the crest of the Andes (S, from 32°51′ S., 69°52′ W.). Cerro de los Penitentes at lower left

189. Talus pits in a cirque head near Puente del Inca (S, from 32°50′ S., 69°58′ W.)

190. A "rock glacier" or a talus-covered glacier at the head of a glaciated valley about 3 miles above Puente del Inca (S, from 32°49′ S., 70°0′ W.)

191. Ice-eroded valleys on the western slope of the Andes about 15 miles southwest of La Cumbre (S, from 32°55′ S., 70°15′ W.)

192. The complex geologic structure of the western slope of the Andes, as seen from a point about 11 miles southeast of Los Andes (S, from 32°56′ S., 70°28′ W.)

193. The upper limits of agriculture on the western slope of the Andes about 25 miles north of Santiago (SE, from 33°5′ S., 70°36′ W.)

194. Irrigated lands at the foot of the Andes, 6 miles northwest of Santiago (ENE, from 33°23′ S., 70°44′ W.). Nevado del Plomo in the background

195. Intensive cultivation on the northern outskirts of Santiago (E, from 33°25′ S., 70°44′ W.)

196. A view over Santiago (ENE)

CENTRAL AND NORTHERN CHILE*

Santiago to Vallenar

THE course from Santiago to Vallenar lay almost due north between the Andes and the Pacific. For the first 75 miles we were too far inland to see the ocean clearly, but thereafter, in flying the west-coast route, the sea on one side and the crest of the western range of the high Andes on the other were visible practically all of the way to Guayaquil, Ecuador.

Santiago lies about 55 miles from the ocean in a down-faulted depression between the relatively low coastal mountains and the Andes.[1] This depression ends about 60 miles north of Santiago, but to the south, in more or less intimate association with similar longitudinal basins, it continues for several hundred miles as the famous Longitudinal Valley or Vale of Chile, in which is concentrated the greater part of Chilean agriculture. In the Santiago region and for about 300 miles to the south, agriculture is dependent upon irrigation water from the Andes, though farther to the south the rainfall increases and irrigation is unnecessary. Immediately south of the irrigated zone is a region especially suited to the culture of wheat, which merges southward into an area adapted to general farming and finally into a cool, moist region primarily devoted to such crops as hay and potatoes.

North of the Santiago region and the valley of the Río Aconcagua the rainfall steadily decreases, not only in the piedmont area but also in the Andes. Thus the rivers available for irrigation become progressively smaller and more widely separated until finally, in northern Chile, none of them extends beyond the immediate base of the mountains. This continuing change northward to the intense aridity of the Atacama Desert is clearly illustrated by the following photographs.

Typical aspects of agriculture in the Santiago basin are illustrated by Figures 197 and 198, taken in the vicinity of the Santiago airport about 6 miles south of the city. In Figure 197 we see from a low altitude the

---

* See Maps V and VI, pp. 286 and 287, below.
[1] For a comprehensive discussion of the geology and physiography of Chile, see J. Brüggen: Grundzüge der Geologie und Lagerstättenkunde Chiles, Math.-Naturwiss. Klasse der Heidelberger Akad. der Wiss., 1934. See also G. M. McBride: Chile: Land and Society, *Amer. Geogr. Soc. Research Series No. 19*, New York, 1936.

details of a Chilean estancia. Vineyards occupy the left half of the picture and grain fields the right. Field irrigation ditches are distinguishable in the latter. The farm buildings, most of which are surrounded by a wall, include a large barn and silo.

The landscape is shown from a greater height in Figure 198. Groups of farm buildings similar to that seen in the preceding picture are recognizable. From about 9 miles north and a little west of Santiago, a view to the west-southwest [199] shows in the foreground the plain of the Santiago depression (or graben), here largely unirrigated. In the background is an eastward-facing fault-block range, rising about 3500 feet above the plain and bounding the basin on the west. Far beyond the range are low cloud banks lying over the ocean or the bordering lowland. Near the northern end of the Santiago basin, where irrigation water from the Andes is not available, dry farming is practiced, as in the district 3 or 4 miles southwest of Chacabuco [200]. In some of the fields that have never been plowed, as well as on the low hills, the native semidesert vegetation appears. In the upper right-hand corner of this view can be seen a large dam, evidently constructed to conserve floodwater.

A stereoscopic view [186] from a position about 29 miles north of Santiago gives a comprehensive impression of the physiography of the Andes in this region. In the foreground is a portion of the northeastern Santiago basin. From it the land rises abruptly to the first of three long ridges of gradually increasing height which intervene between the basin and the high monadnock mass of the Nevado del Plomo on the sky line.

About 45 miles north of Santiago the Río Aconcagua supplies water for extensive irrigation. From a point near the river below San Felipe, a view west-southwest [201] clearly shows the extent of the irrigated area and the nature of the ground reclaimed. The water is used mainly on the lower alluvial slopes bordering the valley. Rail passengers from Santiago to Valparaiso first enter this irrigated area in the Las Mazas-Las Vegas basin, appearing at the upper left of the photograph. The picture emphasizes the dominant north-south trend of the fault-block topography in the region between the Andes and the sea. From 4 miles farther north, and about an equal distance northwest of San Felipe, a view in the opposite direction toward the Andes [202] shows an intensively irrigated portion of the broad structural basin above San Felipe. On the far side of the basin the Andes rise abruptly, probably along a fault which depressed the basin, to a generally accordant sky line at about 16,000 feet, above which Aconcagua towers in solitary grandeur 47 miles from the camera.

For comparison with the aerial photographs of the irrigated valleys of central Chile, a ground view has been included [203]. It shows the irrigated lands of the Las Mazas—Las Vegas basin, as seen from the railroad on the north. Grapes, alfalfa and miscellaneous crops are raised, and the rows of Lombardy poplars lend a typically Chilean touch to the landscape.

For about 70 miles north of the basin east of San Felipe longitudinal structural depressions such as the Vale of Chile do not exist and highlands continue unbroken, though with gradually decreasing elevations, from the Andean front westward to the ocean. In this region valleys are narrow and streams from the mountains are small. In Figure 205 one is looking southwest down a typical valley, that of the Río Petorca, from a position a few miles above the village of Petorca (near the center of the picture). Like nearly all the Andean streams, the Río Petorca has a braided channel that occupies much of the valley floor and thereby greatly decreases the area available for irrigation. As may be seen from this and succeeding pictures, the natural vegetation becomes noticeably sparser and more stunted as we proceed northward.

The broader aspects of the 40-mile strip between our route and the coast are well shown in Figure 184, looking northwest from 2 miles north of latitude 32°. The rocks recognizable beneath the plane ever since leaving the Santiago basin have been a great series of lavas and associated agglomerates, and farther south they seem to have been broken into small fault-block ranges generally parallel to the Andes. Here, however, the north-south alignment of the ridges is less conspicuous, and the topography seems to be governed primarily by normal stream erosion. A short distance east of the course, along a relatively straight front, the land rises abruptly several thousand feet to the high Andes. Although the Andean sky line is generally no more irregular than that shown in this picture, the relief is, of course, much greater.

A view toward the east [204], from about 6 miles beyond the point from which the preceding photograph was taken, shows the strong con-

197. A Chilean estancia surrounded by vineyards and grain fields, on the irrigated plain about 10 miles south-southwest of Santiago (W, from ca. 33°34′ S., 70°44′ W.)

198. An irrigated plain south-southwest of Santiago (W, from ca. 33°31′ S., 70°42′ W.)

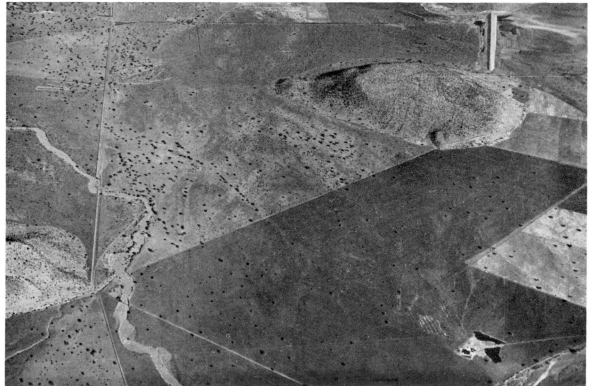

199. A view across an unirrigated portion of the Santiago basin to the bordering mountains on the west, about 9 miles north of Santiago (W, from 33°18′ S., 70°43′ W.)

200. Natural vegetation patterns and dry farming lands near the northern end of the Santiago basin, 25 miles north of Santiago (W, from 33°4′ S., 70°45′ W.). Storage reservoir at upper right

201. The irrigated valley of the Río Aconcagua, as seen from a position about 3 miles southwest of San Felipe (W, from 32°47′ S., 70°48′ W.). The sky line is marked by a fog bank over the Pacific

202. The Andes, surmounted by the huge monadnock peak Aconcagua, as seen from a point 4 miles northwest of San Felipe (ESE, from 32°43′ S., 70°48′ W.)

203. A ground view of the irrigated Las Mazas basin (to the left of center in 201) (SE, from ca. 32°50′ S., 70°59′ W.)

204. The steep-fronted Andean upland surmounted by Cerro Mercedario (E, from 31°53′ S., 70°54′ W.)

205. The narrow, irrigated valley of the Río Petorca, 85 miles north of Santiago (SW, from 32° 14′ S., 70° 52′ W.)

trast in form between the mountains west of the route and those to the east. From the relatively straight front already mentioned, which passes across the foreground of the picture, the Andes rise rather abruptly to elevations about 3000 feet higher than the mountains to the west, and then ascend more gradually, apparently as a maturely dissected upland, to the divide that forms the generally even sky line of the picture at roughly 13,000 to 15,000 feet. The great monadnock, Cerro Mercedario (center), 47 miles away on the Argentine side of the divide, rises to 21,883 feet. Like Aconcagua and the Nevado del Plomo, it stands alone high above the general level of the mountain summits. At the right, in the middle distance, is a "hanging" fragment of an old-age erosion surface, which, beyond the margin of the picture, appeared to arch continuously upward to the general level of the sky line. This condition, of which more was seen farther north, suggests that the high Andes are an uparched portion of an old-age surface of subdued relief produced at a much lower level. In the left foreground and left center of the picture is the irrigated valley of the Río Choapa, the floor of which is here situated at an elevation of about 4000 feet.

Figure 206, looking steeply down to the east-southeast across the Río Chalinga, affords a detailed view of the region along the base of the Andean front. The crudely bedded rocks appear to belong to that great series of lavas, agglomerates, and associated conglomerates already mentioned as dominant all along the route as far as the Peruvian border. Here they dip eastward toward the Andes, as they do rather consistently for 20 miles back, and as they were later observed to do for 30 miles farther to the north. At the right center is part of an extensive remnant of a gently sloping erosion surface about 1000 feet above the stream.

Looking southwest to the ocean, from about 16 miles northeast of Illapel [207], one sees a topography essentially similar to that in Figure 184 except for the fact that near the ocean the north-south alignment of the ranges has reappeared. The Río Illapel at the left carries water enough to irrigate a narrow strip of land along the valley. The city of Illapel, somewhat above and to the left of the center, can be recognized by its street pattern.

An interesting detailed view of an irrigated valley [208] was obtained at the point where a small stream emerges from the higher mountains about 36 miles S. 23° E. from Ovalle. The braided stream, the diversion ditches contouring the hillsides above the irrigated fields, and the apparently neat little village in the center foreground (probably Cogotí) all attract attention.

North of the area shown in the preceding picture the topography to the west of the route became much more subdued. Figure 209, looking west-southwest from a point 18 miles northeast of Ovalle (near the left margin of the picture about halfway from the center to the top), shows in the left background the low old-age relief of the region. In the background, beyond the Altos de Talinai, this smooth upland drops abruptly 1500 to 2000 feet to the ocean. The conservation of floodwater is indicated by the good-sized storage reservoir to the right of the center.

Three miles farther on, we looked eastward toward the Andes [210], which here present the same bold front and relatively even sky line observed farther south. In the foreground sedimentary and volcanic rocks dip somewhat regularly to the east, but farther back the structure is evidently more complex. In the middle distance a fairly distinct topographic bench suggests complications in the physiographic history of the region. North of Ovalle the topography becomes rougher and more like that northwest of Santiago. In Figure 211 one is looking a little south of west from a point 19 miles east of La Serena over the valley of the Río Elqui. Coquimbo lies under the fog in the upper right-hand corner of the picture.

From a point 25 miles northeast of La Serena, looking east toward the Andes [212], we recognize in the foreground the subdued topography of a local basin evidently developed on weak rocks, the abrupt Andean front, and the distant peaks of the high Andes. A little below the center is a small mining camp.

All along the route east and northeast of La Serena numerous prospect pits testify to the extensive mineralization of the region. This condition is also betrayed by the many brilliantly colored areas where the rocks have been altered by the permeation of chemically active mineral and ore-bearing solutions rising at some earlier time from sources deep within the earth. In the deserts of northern Chile and Peru, where the rocks are not obscured by vegetation, a passenger in a plane can recognize such brightly colored mineralized areas from considerable distances. For

206. A typical, narrow irrigated valley at the western base of the Andes, 18 miles east-southeast of Illapel (SE, from 31°43′ S., 70°55′ W.)

207. A view over Illapel to the ocean in the background (WSW, from 31°32′ S., 70°56′ W.)

208. An irrigated valley at the western base of the Andes, about 38 miles south-southeast of Ovalle (E, from 31°5′ S., 70°58′ W.)

209. A view over Ovalle (upper left) and the Altos de Talinai to the Pacific, from a position 18 miles northeast of
       Ovalle (WSW, from 30°27′ S., 70°58′ W.)

210. The dissected western slope of the Andean upland 22 miles northeast of Ovalle (ESE, from 30°25′ S.,
       70°58′ W.)

211. Irrigated valleys and barren mountains, about 22 miles east of Coquimbo (WSW, from 29°56′ S., 70°57′ W.). Fog bank over the ocean

212. A small mining camp (foreground) near the western base of the Andes, about 28 miles northeast of La Serena (E, from 29°41′ S., 70°55′ W.)

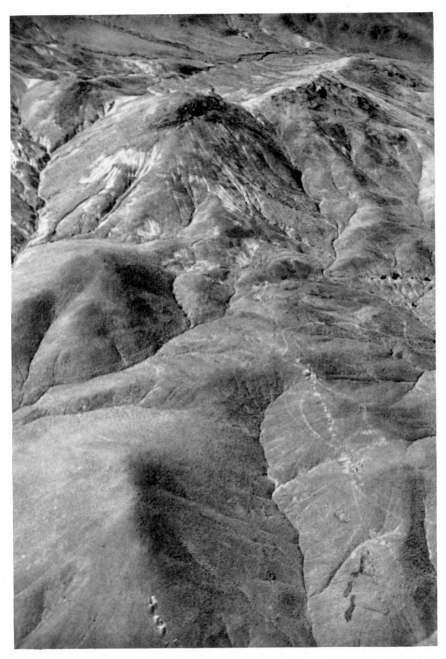

213. Prospect pits along veins in a mineralized area, about 31 miles northeast of La Serena (E, from 29°37′ S., 70°55′ W.)

example, several miles before it was reached, a rounded hill of light-colored rock [213, upper center] was recognizable, because of the brilliantly colored rocks encircling it, as probably an intrusive surrounded by a mineralized zone. As we came nearer, the inference of mineralization was confirmed by numerous prospect pits, which evidently followed veins radiating out from the intrusive. A group of these pits can be seen at the lower left; a continuous row of them, bordered by scattered pits, extends from the right lower corner to the base of the hill, and another row of larger pits nearly at right angles to the first can be recognized above the center near the right margin.

Mining in the deserts of Chile is not merely a matter of finding ore. A factor that has effectively held back the development of all but the richest or largest ore deposits is the difficulty of transport and—much more serious—the difficulty of procuring water.

Northward from Santiago the dominant process involved in molding the landscape has been observed to be erosion—the tearing down by running water of the complex rock structures of the mountains. However, north of latitude 29°, deposition—the filling of structural basins between faulted mountain blocks—gradually assumes a leading role in the area west of the high Andes.

The first indications of this change appeared in the basin of Domeyko about 30 miles south of Vallenar [214]. One is looking west across a basin bordered on the west by a rectilinear scarp that presumably marks the fault responsible for the existence of the basin. The stream draining this depression breaks across the scarp in a gorge and is now engaged in clearing the basin of a former accumulation of relatively recent gravelly sediments. In the area shown in this view most of these recent sediments have already been removed, and the darker bedrock is visible beneath. However, if we turn to the other side of the plane and look eastward toward the Andes [215], we can readily recognize the former outlines of the basin and the nearly horizontal bedding lines of remnants of the recent, presumably fluvial, sediments that formerly filled it.

Within a few minutes, after passing a large mass of intrusive rock to the west of the course, our plane landed for refueling on an extensive gravel terrace overlooking the thriving little city of Vallenar in the irrigated Río Huasco valley.

Vallenar to Antofagasta

Sometimes over the shore line, sometimes as much as 30 miles inland, the flight from Vallenar continued northward parallel with the coast to the Portezuelo airport on the plateau about 8 miles east of Antofagasta. As we take off from Vallenar we have the opportunity of close-up pictures of both the city and the irrigated Huasco Valley. Looking west-southwest as we start across the valley [216], we see fertile stream terraces, which at several levels constitute ideal sites for irrigation, and in the background mountains carved from the large intrusive (monzonite) already mentioned. A few moments later, looking east-southeast up the valley [217], we see Vallenar on the flood plain below the terraces.

North of Vallenar we immediately enter one of the aggraded desert basins [218], which, as already mentioned, are characteristic features of the landscape from here north into Peru. The scattered fault-block ranges, separated by gravel-filled basins and extensive pediments, are almost identical in structure and appearance with those of the Great Basin and southern Arizona in the United States. We are looking west to a range at least partly underlain by a continuation of the large intrusive mass noted south of the valley. Vegetation on the desert plains is scanty and dwarfed.

North of Vallenar the abrupt Andean front disappears. The divide swings farther back from the coast, and the old-age topography of desert ranges and basins gradually gains in altitude eastward until it merges with the high Andean upland. From a position about 22 miles north of Vallenar, a view about S. 55° E. [219] clearly records the change, which will become even more pronounced as we proceed northward.

About 55 miles north of Vallenar, and from that point north for 35 or 40 miles, sand from the coast has been blown inland for many miles, almost completely covering some of the intermontane basins and half burying many of the hills. Twenty-four miles south of the Río Copiapó and 17 miles from the coast, Figure 220 shows an old-age hilly topography being buried beneath wind-blown sand. All of the region from this point north to beyond the Río Copiapó and west to the coast is in this condition, except that near the coast the covering of sand is more nearly complete. It is an interesting fact that in the entire flight from

Santiago to northern Peru, part of it over one of the driest deserts in the world, drifting sand in significant quantities was seen only in areas where it obviously had been blown inland from the seashore. Its distribution with respect to the larger rivers suggests that it may have been carried by them to the sea, distributed along the coast by the waves, and then picked up by the winds.

Beyond Vallenar, the Río Copiapó, 85 miles to the north, is the only stream in a distance of over 600 miles carrying enough water to permit irrigation in the vicinity of the coast. Looking down the Río Copiapó where we crossed it 20 miles from the sea [221], we find it following a braided channel between barren hills and alluvial slopes. Irrigation is confined to small areas on the flood plain.

The rugged nature of the coastal region in this part of Chile is well shown in Figure 222, looking west-southwest toward the coast from 12 miles inland, 40 miles north of the Río Copiapó. The rocks appear to be mainly igneous, and the mountains drop abruptly to the sea, though displaying no evidence of structure parallel to the coast. White sand from the ocean chokes the valley heads on the peak in the middle distance some 3000 feet above the sea. Another glimpse of the coast, 15 miles south of Chañaral at Punta Flamenco [223], shows the mountains gradually decreasing in height toward the sea and a coast line suggestive of drowning.

Because of the lack of vegetation in the Atacama Desert of northern Chile, the surface geology in many places is fully revealed to a passenger in a plane. Six to nine miles east-northeast from the port of Chañaral is a most striking geological phenomenon [224]. A large mass of white rock (lower two-thirds of the picture), probably granite, is crisscrossed by an intricate network of dark-colored dikes. At some time when the present surface was far underground, molten rock of a dark color was forced into cracks and fissures in the light-colored rock and there hardened. These fillings are the dikes, which have finally been revealed by prolonged and deep erosion. The dikes are not confined to the white rock but may be seen, though less conspicuously, also in the darker rocks of the background. In the absence of familiar objects such as houses or trees for comparison, it is difficult to judge scale in desert pictures such as this. However, the dikes probably reach a maximum thickness of more than 100 feet. The light-colored area in the foreground is rough and hilly, with a probable relief of several hundred feet; the valley in the background is at least 4 or 5 miles away.

Numerous dikes were first noticed about 75 miles to the south, and they have gradually increased in abundance northward. If the reader will reëxamine Figures 222 and 223, he will recognize them at once. Dikes in large numbers are found at least as far north as Taltal, and locally nearly to Antofagasta. Can it be significant that this region, intensely fissured and seamed by dikes, lies adjacent to, and approximately coextensive with, the Richards Deep, in which the ocean floor drops to 25,000 feet below sea level only 45 miles offshore? Are the dikes perhaps tensional phenomena in the crust related to the formation of the deep?

From a point 45 miles south of Taltal, a view directed a little south of east [225] reveals the nature of the area from 10 miles east of the coast to the high Andes on the sky line. It is an old-age region of low ranges and intervening desert basins rising gradually eastward. This surface, warped rather sharply upward without change in character, forms the Andean upland. The writer rode on a train for 13 hours across this district, in the middle background and farther north, without seeing a growing plant of any kind except at some of the railway stations where wells or tanks supplied water for a few flowers or shrubs. This region, the heart of the Atacama, is an absolutely barren desert, yet it is rich in minerals.

About 10,000 feet above the sea, somewhere in the extreme right background of Figure 225, is the great Potrerillos camp of the Andes Copper Company, a part of which is shown in Figure 226. This ground picture [226] is introduced to show one of the physiographic evidences of the relatively recent upwarping of an old-age desert topography, such as that shown in Figure 225 to form the upland of the high Andes. Such crustal deformation is clearly suggested by the sharp dissection of the gravel deposits that formerly filled the basins between the old-age mountains. The precipitous canyon beyond the camp is cut about 1500 feet below the level of the former basin floor.

A detailed view of the typical physiography in this region is shown in Figure 227, looking west from a position 32 miles south of Taltal. The alluviated valley at the upper left is similar to those seen in Figure 225, except that it is smaller than many of them. A short distance below the

center is a typical small desert mining camp, and a still smaller one appears on the hilltop a little below and to the right.

The coast about 6 miles southwest of Taltal [228] seems to have been
formed by the submergence of an old-age mountainous region of complex structure similar to that which now borders it. The trend of the
coast line is entirely independent of structure, as is shown by the fact
that the bedded rocks in the middle distance strike directly into the sea.
A slight recent uplift is, however, suggested by the narrow platform
bordering the shore.

The city of Taltal [229] is situated on a narrow shelf, like those seen in
the preceding picture, at the foot of a high escarpment that faces the
ocean for the next 90 miles. The escarpment, which has many features
suggesting that it is a fault scarp, rises in places as an almost sheer cliff
6000 feet above the water. Taltal is a bleak and treeless desert port serving the copper and nitrate industries. Looking back to the southeast from
a point 33 miles north of Taltal [230], we see the southern end of the
higher part of this scarp, with an old-age topography above and behind
it. At its base a very short talus and alluvial fan slope leads down to a low
rocky cliff, against which the waves are breaking.

Fifty miles north of Taltal, as we fly directly over the coast at nearly
6000 feet [185], the top of the scarp seems less than a mile away, and its
higher parts are at our level. Back of the scarp is a subdued, old-age landscape of moderate relief cut off abruptly at the edge of the escarpment.
On its seaward face the rocks, which appear to be metamorphic (gneisses
or schists), are so fresh that they still retain their unweathered steel-blue
color.

It is somewhat surprising, in a land as dry as the Atacama Desert, to
find almost every detail of the topography a product of either erosion or
deposition by running water. Only where wind is carrying sand inland
from the sea [220, 222] and — of minor importance — on the finer soils of
the central parts of some of the bolsons, or desert basins, were exceptions
noted. To emphasize the dominance of running water in molding the
landscape in one of the driest of deserts, several photographs similar to
Figure 231, looking west from a point 14 miles S. 22°E. of Antofagasta,
were taken. On soft shales such as those in the foreground, stream-carved
topography is perfectly developed. On other rocks, such as granites or

lavas, the sculpturing is of coarser texture, but little, if at all, different from that which would occur on the same rocks in a moister climate.

Antofagasta to Arica

From the airport 8 miles east of Antofagasta we flew northwestward to the coast and thence close offshore to the mouth of the Río Loa, at which point we turned inland and followed the western side of the Pampa del Tamarugal to Arica.

In our description of the coastal region from Santiago to Antofagasta, much was said about faults and fault-block ranges, but, with minor exceptions north of Vallenar, no indications were noted of any very recent movement along the faults. From Antofagasta north to Arica, however, the faulting movements are still actively in progress and no trained observer flying over the region could fail to see many evidences of them. For instance, about 2 miles west of the Portezuelo airport of Antofagasta [232], the alluvial fans along the base of the mountains to the west (Sierra Ancla) have been broken and the western side relatively uplifted 30 to 50 feet along a fault that was seen on the ground to extend for at least 15 miles north and south. In places, as in this picture, it dies out and then reappears, *en échelon*, a few hundred feet to one side. The recency of this fault is attested by the slight modification by erosion.

As we turn northwest across the Sierra Ancla about 6 miles east-northeast of Antofagasta, we look south along the range [233] to find that it appears to be a single mountain block composed of the extremely thick series of purplish lavas and associated rocks already mentioned. These rocks are tilted rather steeply to the west-southwest, striking at an angle into the line of the fault described above, which passes diagonally upward to the right across the upper left-hand corner of the picture. They are cut by numerous dikes of a white rock, probably either white granite or pegmatite.

Antofagasta, one of the principal ports of northern Chile, which serves as the outlet for the large Antofagasta and Aguas Blancas nitrate districts and as the terminus of the railroad from Bolivia, is seen partly under a cloud at the right as we approach the coast [234]. The city is built at the foot of the Sierra Ancla on a platform, similar to that seen at Taltal, formed by a recent slight relative emergence of the land. An interesting

and significant physiographic feature is the long desert basin that seems
to be warped down from an elevation of more than 2000 feet [233, upper
left] to, and perhaps below, sea level.

Looking inland 8 miles north-northeast of Antofagasta [235], we see
an old-age topography of subdued ranges, bolsons, and extensive pediments rising gradually to the Andean upland on the sky line.

The peninsula north of Antofagasta [236, 237] is the projecting top of
a faulted mountain range, such as we have been seeing, partly consumed
at an earlier time by the waves of the sea and connected with the mainland by a strip of low land that may, in part, be an unsubmerged intermontane bolson. At both its northern and southern ends, the low land
has been extended by relatively recent marine deposition. Morro Moreno
[236] at the south end (4163 ft.), is bordered on the near side (east) by
an extensive pediment partly veneered with gravel. At its upper end,
near the base of the mountains, a recent fault movement[2] has displaced the
fan gravels along a scarp similar to that shown in Figure 232. Somewhere
near the left center of Figure 236 is the site recently chosen by Pan
American-Grace Airways for its new Antofagasta airport. Except for
the small peak of Cerro el Morro, or Morro de Mejillones (2377 feet),
the entire northern end of the peninsula [237] was beveled and terraced
by the waves as it was uplifted in stages and simultaneously slivered by
faulting. This is clearly indicated in the left half of the picture. The
highest marine terrace surrounding the peak is situated at an elevation of
1920 feet, and 8 lower terraces have been mapped. Important deposits of
guano once existed on these terraces; the richest accumulation was found
on the highest level, evidently formed when Morro de Mejillones was a
small island rising about 450 feet above the sea.[3] The city of Mejillones
lies on the bay in as dreary a location as could well be imagined. Faint
curving lines on the plain in the foreground and behind the city mark
former shore lines, progressively abandoned as the land has slowly risen.

For 35 miles north of the latitude of Mejillones the coastal escarpment,
rising for the first 3000 feet as an abrupt, almost straight wall, is composed of purplish-red lavas and associated tuffs and agglomerates. Beyond
that for the next 70 miles it consists mainly of granites, gneisses, and other

---

[2] This feature was observed on the ground before the flight.
[3] For additional information, see Brüggen, *op. cit.*, pp. 142 and 273.

"basement" rocks, together with smaller masses of resistant sediments. About 10 miles north of Tocopilla the coastal escarpment, here composed of the "basement" rocks, is particularly abrupt [238], rising at Cerro Tolar to 7529 feet less than 4 miles from the coast. At the top is a late mature to old-age upland of moderate relief.

A portion of the surface of that upland is seen in Figure 239, as we look northeast from a position over the coast 27 miles north of Tocopilla. Its general plateau-like character is evident. On the sky line are the even-crested high Andes, surmounted at the right by snow-clad volcanoes near the Bolivian border. Between the plateau and the Andes is the broad Longitudinal Depression, here occupied by the lower course of the Río Loa. This depression continues northward through the Pampa del Tamarugal to Arica and southward to the basins southeast of Antofagasta. In it are most of the great sodium nitrate deposits of northern Chile.[4] In the foreground, clouds, such as frequently hang over the ocean along the north Chilean and Peruvian coasts in winter, penetrate a few miles inland before being evaporated by the dry air of the desert. In the nitrate district the heavy fogs (camanchacas) produced by such clouds constitute almost the sole supply of moisture, which is believed to be great enough at times, however, to play an important part in dissolving and redepositing the soluble salts in the surface rocks and thereby concentrating the sodium nitrate.

Turning inland about 50 miles north of Tocopilla, we travel only a few miles before seeing additional striking evidence of the seeming instability of the earth's crust in northern Chile [240]. Here, on a line running up and to the left from the lower center of the picture, the surface appears to have been broken along a fault and the left side dropped down in relation to the right. Along the break, the ground is extensively cracked and fissured. If one imagines hot, ore-bearing solutions finding their way toward the surface along such a fault and depositing their ores in any available fissures, it is not difficult to understand why many ore deposits are located along lines of faulting. In the background the Longitudinal Depression can be dimly seen.

Six miles farther on (70 miles S. 10°E. of Iquique), the flat surface of

---

4 John L. Rich: The Nitrate District of Tarapacá, Chile: An Aerial Traverse, *Geogr. Rev.*, Vol. 31, 1941, pp. 1–22.

214. The erosional excavation of a portion of the sediment-filled Domeyko basin, about 30 miles south of Vallenar (W, from 29°1′ S., 70°50′ W.)

215. The eastern side of the Domeyko basin backed by the western front of the Andean upland, 26 miles south of Vallenar (SE, from 28°55′ S., 70°49′ W.)

216. Irrigated stream terraces at Vallenar (WSW, from 28°34′ S., 70°47′ W.)

217. Looking up the Río Huasco valley over Vallenar (E, from 28°34′ S., 70°47′ W.)

218. A typical desert basin and a bordering coastal range, as seen from a low altitude about 7 miles north of Vallenar (W, from 28°29′ S., 70°46′ W.)

219. A rugged region of broken ranges rising gradually toward the crest of the Andes, 22 miles north of Vallenar (SE, from 28°15′ S., 70°44′ W.)

220. Sand blown inland from the coast mantling the hills about 61 miles north of Vallenar (W, from 27°42′ S., 70°41′ W.)

221. The Río Copiapó and its flood plain 20 miles from the sea (W, from 27°22′ S., 70°39′ W.)

222. Barren coastal mountains 40 miles north of the Río Copiapó (W, from 26°46′ S., 70°37′ W.)

223. A view toward the ocean 15 miles south of Chañaral (W, from ca. 26°34′ S., 70°36′ W.). The coastal submergence suggested here by the presence of alluviated valleys presents an interesting contrast to the relative emergence indicated by trenched valleys farther north

224. A complexly interwoven pattern of dark-colored dikes in a mass of white rock, probably granite, 8 miles northeast of Chañaral (E, from 26°18′ S., 70°35′ W.)

225. A succession of old-age ranges and desert basins rising gradually to the high Andes, as seen from a position about 20 miles north-northeast of Chañaral (ESE, from 26°6′ S., 70°34′ W.)

226. Sharply dissected bolson deposits around the Potrerillos mining camp (NE, from ca. 26°31′ S., 69°31′ W.)

227. Mining camps (center foreground) in a typical desert area 32 miles south of Taltal (W, from 25°54′ S., 70°34′ W.)

228. A low marine terrace along the coast about 6 miles southwest of Taltal (WSW, from 25°30′ S., 70°33′ W.). Rock structures appear to strike directly into the sea

229. The port of Taltal, an outlet for hinterland copper and nitrate industries (SW, from 25°26′ S., 70°33′ W.)

230. An imposing coastal escarpment 33 miles north of Taltal (SE, from 24°57′ S., 70°33′ W.)

231. Minutely dissected desert topography, viewed from a point 14 miles south-southeast of Antofagasta (W, from 23°50′ S., 70°20′ W.)

232. A recent fault scarp cutting the alluvial fans along the eastern slope of the Sierra Ancla about 7 miles east of Antofagasta (W, from 23°40′ S., 70°18′ W.)

233. The crest of the Sierra Ancla, a monoclinal fault block composed largely of tilted lavas, as seen from a point about 6 miles east of Antofagasta (S, from 23°37′ S., 70°20′ W.)

234. Antofagasta, situated on an uplifted wave-cut platform at the foot of the Sierra Ancla (SSW, from 23°34′ S., 70°22′ W.)

235. A view across coastal mountains and broad desert basins to the Andes, from a point 8 miles north-northwest of Antofagasta (ESE, from 23°32′ S., 70°22′ W.)

236. Morro Moreno, as seen from a position 18 miles north of Antofagasta (WSW, from 23°23′ S., 70°22′ W.)

237. Mejillones and the elevated marine terraces of Cerro el Morro (W, from 23°4′ S., 70°21′ W.)

238–240. (See opposite page)

a desert basin is cracked and fissured in a striking manner, though no visible net displacement has occurred [241]. By comparison with the size of the adjacent mule trails it is estimated that some of the fissures are as much as 50 feet wide. In a distance of 22 miles north from the position of Figure 240 five of six pictures (not here reproduced) show such fissuring. Figure 242, 10 miles north of Figure 241, shows the results of similar fissuring at an earlier date. The curious features here are either dikes of igneous rock intruded into fissures, or veins of mineral harder than the surrounding rocks deposited in the fissures from solution and etched into relief by weathering and erosion. This picture is interesting also in showing the absolute barrenness of the desert.

Figure 243, looking westward from a point about 55 miles S. 19°E. of Iquique, presents a puzzle. It shows the surface of one of the dried-up salt lakes (*salares*) which typically occupy the bottoms of the desert basins in northern Chile. The smooth light-colored areas are believed to be a crust, perhaps of anhydrite, which is collapsing as a result of the withdrawal or shrinkage of the material beneath. Shadows indicate that the darkest patches within the collapsed areas have sunk still lower below their surroundings. This phenomenon deserves further study on the ground.

We now turn farther to the northeast and then to the north and fly along the western border of the Longitudinal Depression (Pampa del Tamarugal), the undrained lowest part of which is occupied by the large Salar de Pintados, 3200 feet above the sea. The largest nitrate deposits of the northern, or Tarapacá, field are situated on the lower slopes of the coastal "range" or upland bordering the western side of this salar and the continuation of its depression northward.[5]

A typical portion of the nitrate district is pictured in Figure 244, looking west-southwest near the western center of the Salar de Pintados

[5] For a more detailed account of the nitrate district and additional photographs, see Rich, *loc. cit.*

TITLES TO FIGURES 238–240.

238. At Cerro Tolar, 10 miles north of Tocopilla, an old-age upland drops off abruptly along the coast in a 6000-foot cliff (ENE, from 22°0′ S., 70°13′ W.)
239. The intricately, but not deeply, dissected coastal upland south of the Río Loa (NE, from 21°42′ S., 70°8′ W.)
240. Fissuring along a fault in the coastal upland, about 57 miles north-northeast of Tocopilla (ENE, from 21°18′ S., 70°0′ W.)

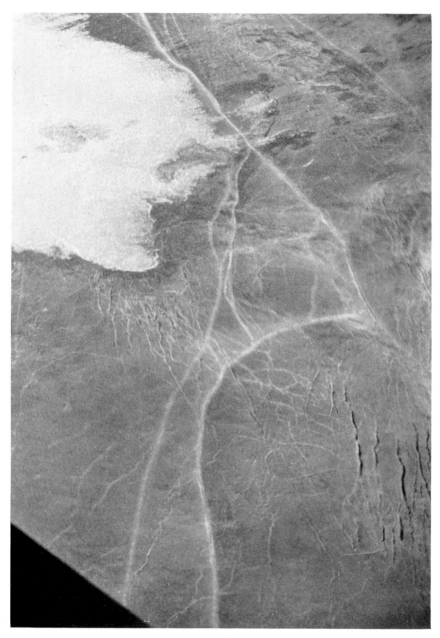

241. Earthquake fissures on a desert plain, 62 miles north-northeast of Tocopilla (SE, from ca. 21°13′ S., 69°58′ W.)

(about 32 miles S. 58°E. of Iquique). At the left is the flat surface of the salar, on which nitrate is never found. On the lower slopes of the adjoining hills are the nitrate diggings, easily recognizable because the smooth surface soil of the hill slopes has been overturned and reworked in the

242. Dikes or veins of resistant rock etched into relief by the weathering and erosion of the weaker materials surrounding them, 62 miles south-southeast of Iquique (W, from ca. 21°5′ S., 69°55′ W.)

process of selecting the nitrate. The nitrate occurs as one member of a layered crust of salts that has accumulated in the upper few feet of the soil and surficial rock debris. In the center is a large nitrate *oficina*, distinguished by the large flat-topped dump of refuse from which the nitrate has been extracted and by the buildings housing the extraction plant and the workers.

The details of an oficina are more clearly shown in a view from nearly

overhead [246]. At the left is the flat surface of the salar with its numerous roads, railroads, and trails; to the right is an area from which the
nitrate has been removed, leaving the ground in the characteristically
disordered condition already noted; and in the center is the oficina. At its
left is the large, high dump; in the near center are the buildings housing
the extraction machinery, the evaporation and storage tanks for the
brines, and the platforms for drying the nitrate before shipment; and
farther back are the office buildings and the quarters for the workmen.
This plant was apparently not in operation at the time the picture was
taken.

On the opposite side of the plane, beyond the broad, flat expanse of
the Salar de Pintados [245, 29 miles S. 69°E. of Iquique], an enormous
gravel apron of coalescing alluvial fans rises gradually up the distant
western slopes of the Andes. The nearer high range forms the sky line,
and on the second range, 100 miles away, stand several snow-clad volcanoes. The gravels of the great alluvial fans continue westward under
the Salar de Pintados and in this region carry fresh water from the
mountains so close to the surface that a thin forest of mimosas once covered part of the plain. Water can be found at shallow depths in wells,
and some attempts at fruit culture have been made on the part of the
plain near the center of the picture.

In Figure 247, looking south-southwest from a point about 34 miles N.
38°E. of Iquique, are combined nearly all the characteristic features of
physiography and culture in the nitrate district of Tarapacá: the desolate
nitrate town, probably Negreiros, on the flat surface of the salar in the
foreground, entirely bare of vegetation with the possible exception of a
few trees in some of the patios; the nitrate diggings on the lower slopes
of the coast range bordering the salar; the oficinas among the workings
with their characteristic grouping; the broad mule trails leading northwestward across the desert to the coastal port of Caleta Buena; and,
finally, the monadnock-strewn, pedimented, old-age surface of the coast
range (or, probably more properly, coastal upland), which, just beyond
the sky line, drops abruptly 3000 feet to the ocean.

North of the exploited nitrate fields, the Longitudinal Depression continues with features similar to those observed farther south except that
here the streams from the Andes cross the depression and the coastal

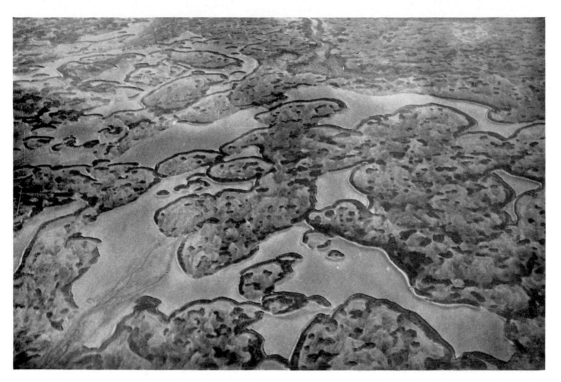

243. Interesting surface patterns on a salar, or dried-up salt lake, 55 miles south-southeast of Iquique (W, from ca. 20°58′ S., 69°53′ W.)

244. A nitrate oficina on the western margin of the Salar de Pintados, as seen from a point 31 miles south-east of Iquique (WSW, from 20°28′ S., 69°45′ W.)

245. A view across the broad Salar de Pintados to the Andes (SE, from 20°22′ S., 69°45′ W.)

246. A nitrate oficina 32 miles northeast of Iquique (SW, from 19°54′ S., 69°49′ W.). The extraction plant, waste dump, and dug-over nitrate ground are especially characteristic

247. A synoptic view of the geography of the Chilean nitrate district from a position 34 miles northeast of Iquique (SW, from 19°49′ S., 69°51′ W.). The towns, oficinas, nitrate diggings, desert trails, salar, and old-age topography of the coast range are all distinctive features of the region

248. A peculiar stream meander on the surface of a salar, about 53 miles north-northeast of Iquique (SSW, from 19°28′ S., 70°0′ W.)

uplands to the ocean and are beginning to trench the basin fillings, as is shown in Figure 250, looking northeast from a point 17 miles east of Pisagua over the Quebrada de Retamilla in the middle distance and the Quebrada de Tana or Camiña beyond. The trails converging toward the points where the streams leave the mountains bear witness to the thou-

249.   The course of the Quebrada de Tana cut into the bed of an old salar in the Longitudinal Depression, about 54 miles north of Iquique (SW, from 19° 27′ S., 70° 1′ W.)

sands of mule and burro loads of fruit, alfalfa, and other produce that have gone down to the nitrate towns and oficinas from the narrow irrigated valleys at the western base of the Andes.

On the flats between the canyons that trench the northern end of the Longitudinal Depression — Figure 248, looking southwest from a position about 3 miles south of the Quebrada de Tana — collapse features similar to those of Figure 243 indicate the former presence of salars. In this picture a temporary stream has entrenched a meandering course into such a flat and incidentally has produced a most curious feature at the more distant of the meanders. An enlargement of this portion of the

250. Mule or burro trails crossing the dissected piedmont fans near the western base of the Andes (NE, from 19°33′ S., 69°58′ W.)

251. A view toward the Andes across the inter-canyon remnants of the flat bottom of the Longitudinal Depression from a point 60 miles south-southeast of Arica (NE, from 19°18′ S., 70°4′ W.)

picture (inset) fails to provide a clue as to how such a feature could be formed.

The pitted surface of the former salar is clearly seen in crossing the Quebrada de Tana [249]. Beyond the flat, we see the lower hills of the cloud-covered coast range, through which the stream has cut a deep, narrow gorge. In the canyon, in the middle distance, the contact is distinct between the light-colored sediments constituting the basin filling and the darker old rocks below. The line of contact along the walls of the canyon proves that in this region no fault exists along the western margin of the Longitudinal Depression and that the sediments underlying the flats lap up on, and have buried, the lower part of the tilted old-age surface of the coastal upland.

Farther north the canyons become deeper and wider and the flat remnants of the basin filling between them more mesa-like. A view typifying all of this region for the next 60 miles north to Arica is afforded by Figure 251, looking northeastward toward the Andes from a point 24 miles N. 26° E. of Pisagua. In the foreground is a part of the Pampa de Tana, one of the remnants of the salar bottom converted into a mesa by the canyon cutting. It is crossed by the now familiar mule trails and, beginning at the left, by what appears to be a fault that has broken the level summit of the mesa so recently that the surface is still cracked in a manner similar to that shown in Figure 240.

Five miles farther north (55 miles from Arica), a much larger recent fault has displaced the surface [252]. Looking a little south of west, we see a fault scarp, which, as we crossed it, showed the same type of fissuring as that in Figure 240. On the downthrow side, in the center and background, is a good example of the old-age mountain topography characteristic of the coastal uplands. In the lower left is the pitted surface of a salar.

Some of the northern canyons crossing the Longitudinal Depression carry sufficient water as far west as the line of flight to permit the irrigation of narrow strips along the canyon bottoms.

PERU*

Arica to Arequipa

O N the 185-mile early morning flight from Arica to Arequipa, the characteristic coastal cloud layer at about 5000 feet obscured much of the ground, but our disappointment was partly compensated by the beauties of the sunrise over the Andes as seen from above the boiling upper surface of the clouds [253].

Before going into the clouds, we flew out over the coast line and about 9 miles north of Arica observed elevated beaches about a mile behind a swampy foreshore, the width of which increased somewhat northward. The sloping surface of the pampa, the northward continuation of the Longitudinal Depression, appeared to bend gradually down to the shore as if the bottom of the depression had here been warped down to sea level and its western side submerged.

Seventy-six miles north of Arica, and again at 106 miles, two photographs, of which one is here reproduced, show the old-age tops of mountain blocks projecting above the clouds. The northernmost of these [254] is sharply bounded on the north and west by rectilinear lines that appear to be faults. The fact that erosion is only beginning to work backward into the blocks indicates the recency of their uplift. Both blocks, according to the map, appear to be on the western side of a continuation of the Longitudinal Depression which seems finally to pass into the sea at the mouth of the Río Tambo.

Looking forward a little east of north from a point 120 miles north of Arica [255], we see an intricately dissected slope rising gradually and rather evenly to the crest of the Andes at the right. On the sky line at the left and center are the three great volcanic masses near Arequipa—Chachani at the extreme left, Misti in the center, and Pichu-Pichu at the right (center of picture). Of these, Misti is still fresh and unscarred by erosion, but Chachani and Pichu-Pichu have lost most of their original form through intense glacial erosion, and possibly partly as a result of explosion.

Four miles farther north [256], we look eastward toward the Andes over an intricately but not deeply dissected slope, for many miles rising

---

* See Maps VI and VII, pp. 286 and 287, below.

252. A recently formed fault scarp in the coastal uplands 55 miles south-southeast of Arica (W, from 19°13′ S., 70°5′ W.)

253. A sunrise over the Andes, as it appeared 67 miles northwest of Arica above a coastal cloud bank in southern Peru (E, from ca. 17°41′ S., 70°56′ W.)

gradually, and then more abruptly, to the high Andes on the sky line. The fine-textured topography in the foreground resembles that characteristic of shale or clay. From this and adjoining pictures not here reproduced, it seems most probable that the dissected slope represents an old-age surface on granite or metamorphic rock which was once deeply covered by alluvial material and was then uplifted and tilted westward, and that at the present time the alluvial material has been partly eroded away, exposing the underlying hard rock in places and imposing on it, temporarily where exposed, the fine-textured drainage pattern inherited from the previously superimposed claylike material. Some of the other pictures quite definitely reveal intermediate stages of this interesting history. In strong contrast with the shallow valleys on the sloping surface pictured here, is the deep, narrow canyon of the Río Tambo, a portion of which can be seen in the upper left-hand corner of the picture.

More picturesque, although physiographically perhaps not so instructive, is the view toward the low morning sun up the canyon of the Río Tambo [257]. The fog of the coastal cloud bank lies like a body of water in the bottom of the canyon. About 65 miles away on the sky line is the crest of the western or maritime cordillera of the Andes, rising 16,000 feet above the sea.

From the Río Tambo to Arequipa the rock seemed to be mainly of a granitic type and is definitely so where we crossed the western margin of the Cerros de la Caldera. The physiography is generally similar to that farther south.

Arequipa to Lima

On the flight from Arequipa west and then northwest to Lima, our route lay a few miles to the west of the Andean mountain front, approaching the sea closely between latitude $15\frac{1}{2}°$ and $16°$ S. and again north of latitude $13°$ S., but elsewhere 10 to 35 miles inland. Through an unfortunate misunderstanding, my camera was not available for the first 250 miles of the course (to $15°11'$ S., $74°47'$ W.), and consequently only a brief word picture of that part of the route can be given, tied by reference letters to the flight map on page 286.

After crossing at *A* a strip of granite hills about 6 miles wide, apparently a northwestward continuation of the granites of the Cerros de la

Caldera, we came over bedded sediments resting on the granite, the smooth seaward-sloping surface of which is thinly veneered with drifting sand in small crescent dunes—the Pampa de Vitor. Thence for about 140 miles we flew, at distances from the sea gradually decreasing from 30 miles to about 6 miles, over the sloping surface of a series of pampas,

254. A rectilinear block mountain rising above the clouds on the western side of the continuation of the Longitudinal Depression in southern Peru, seen from a point about 106 miles northwest of Arica (SW, from 17°14′ S., 71°17′ W.)

which at one time formed a continuous plain, but which are now separated by canyons 1000 to about 4000 feet deep cut by the Río Majes, the Río Ocoña, the Quebrada de Atico, the Río de Chaparra, the Río de Lomas, and smaller streams. Geologically and physiographically the whole region is a unit, the broader features of which are shown diagrammatically in the profile on p. 288. A narrow coastal plain is bounded inland by an escarpment, possibly an old sea cliff, rising abruptly 1500 to more than 2500 feet to the edge of the pampa, which here is a sloping plain ascending toward the mountains and somewhat dissected at the front and along the canyons. Mountainward, as seen from the air, the pampa generally seems to merge into an old-age erosion surface on the mountains, which gradually becomes steeper as it arches up toward the summit of the Andes. Locally, however, as at *B*, the pampas are separated from the mountains by subsequent valleys and high inward facing

255. A group of great volcanoes towering above the general Andean sky line in southern Peru, as seen from a point 48 miles south-southeast of Arequipa (N, from 17°5′ S., 71°24′ W.)

cuestas. The steep walls of the canyons reveal perfect cross sections of a few hundred to a thousand feet or more of relatively even-bedded unconsolidated Tertiary sediments resting unconformably on an uneven surface of older crystalline and metamorphic rocks in the same way as at the northern end of the Longitudinal Depression south of Arica [249]. In fact, in its broader aspects, this region is essentially similar to that and also, in all probability, to the region between Arica and Arequipa discussed in connection with Figure 256. In this region, however, the equivalent of the coast range, although present, is poorly developed.[1] Only locally in flying across it does one see coastal hills interrupting the smooth seaward slope of the pampas before they break off at the coastal escarpment.

After crossing the Río de Lomas about 9 miles from the sea, we devi-

---

[1] For detailed maps and a description of a part of this region see Isaiah Bowman: The Andes of Southern Peru, Amer. Geogr. Soc., New York, 1916, especially pp. 110–120 and 225–273.

256. An intricately dissected land surface rising gradually eastward to the high
Andes, 45 miles south of Arequipa (ENE, from 17°2′ S., 71°26′ W.)

257. The fog-filled canyon of the Río Tambo, 42 miles south of Arequipa (ESE, from 17°0′ S., 71°28′ W.)

ated to the east of a straight line of flight and in so doing observed some puzzling markings on the plains near Nazca. We at first flew parallel to the Andean front where it curves eastward in the broad arc drained by the Río Grande, and then north and northwest, regaining our direct course at Ica.[2] In this region the top of the Andes, at an altitude between 14,000 and 15,000 feet, is remarkably even [258]. The appearance of this portion of the range suggests that a rolling old-age plain of moderate relief has been arched up rather steeply at the front and less steeply behind to form the Andean highland and has since been frayed along the edge by erosion and deeply trenched by the canyons of the larger streams. All along the mountain front from here to Lima, remnants of the warped old-age surface can be seen on the spurs between the canyons. On the top of the spur to the right is an enormous mass of sand, presumably blown inland from the coast and lodged in this surprising spot through some freak of relief-controlled wind currents. Several similar large sand masses were noted between Arequipa and this point.

In the area drained by tributaries of the Río Grande the extensive alluvial-fan surfaces at the foot of the mountains [259] are covered with interesting markings that excite much curiosity on the part of air travelers. Most of them are obviously mule or burro trails, but not all can be so easily explained. Some are perfectly straight for 2 or 3 miles. One of these spreads out into a narrow wedge at the lower right of the photograph. Others, not shown in this picture, are rectangular areas one-half to three-quarters of a mile long and a few hundred feet wide, bordered by low embankments. Presumably some of these markings date back to the time of the Incas or even earlier, but others are certainly modern. A ground study guided by aerial photographs would be interesting.

Six miles beyond the position of the preceding picture, Figure 260 shows a stream typical of those which in this region emerge from the mountains and converge to form the Río Grande. Most of them furnish enough water for considerable irrigation, as they evidently did also in Inca and pre-Inca times.

In this region a sandy desert plain, 30 to 45 miles wide, lies between the sea and the base of the Andes. Its general appearance is indicated by

---

[2] Because of the lack of definite check points recognizable on the map, locations in this area are only approximate.

Figure 261, looking south-southwest from a point about 22 miles southeast of Ica. In the foreground is the irrigated valley of the Río de Ica, and beyond it the arid plain. In the region east of Ica [262] the Andes, as farther south [258], appear to have been reduced to old age and subsequently uparched and dissected. A similar condition persists all the way to the latitude of Lima.

Having become familiar with the aerial aspect of the Andes and their irrigated valleys, the reader may be interested in their appearance from the ground [263]. This is a view eastward from the temple grounds of the ruined Inca and pre-Inca city of Pachacamac, about 15 miles southeast of Lima. The valley of the Río de Lurin in the middle distance was irrigated by the pre-conquest Indians who built their city on the hill slopes adjoining the irrigated areas. Many of the coastal valleys appear to have been as fully irrigated and as intensively cultivated by the Incas and their predecessors as they are today.

Lima to Trujillo

From Lima to Trujillo the route lay close to the seashore along an almost straight line bearing approximately N. 27°W. Figure 264, looking east to the Andes 68 miles along the route, presents a view typical of the first hundred miles north of Lima. To this point the characteristic low coastal cloud bank hid the ground below, but above the clouds the Andes rose as a great even-topped wall beginning about 25 miles to the east and culminating 65 to 70 miles away. As the clouds cleared, a foothill belt of moderate relief was revealed, much of it far advanced in the erosion cycle, as is shown in this picture. All the way from Lima to Trujillo the coastal area is extremely arid.

At intervals rivers from the mountains cross the foothills to the sea, supplying water for the irrigation of valleys such as that pictured in Figure 265, believed to be the lower course of the Río de la Fortaleza. Sugar is the principal crop. The limited area that can be irrigated and the barren nature of the adjoining desert are well illustrated.

Twenty-one miles farther on, and 137 miles along the route from Lima, Figure 266, looking east, presents a somewhat different aspect of the Andes where their spurs descend gradually to the ocean. The complexity of the geological structure is indicated in the foreground. In this vicinity, for 10 miles or more to the south and for at least 50 miles to the north, thick masses of tilted and faulted stratified rocks were observed.

From about 9°45′ S. northward to Trujillo great quantities of sand are being blown far inland from the coast. About 5 miles northwest of Casma (9°25′ S.), a wave-cut platform strongly swept by sand-bearing winds [267] shows features typical of much of the region. We are looking a little north of east. The sand is being blown inland by the prevailing southwest winds, forming numerous small barchans and, in the upper left, larger sand ripples. The curving patterns formed by the sand as it is drifted by wind currents deflected by the near-by topography is an interesting feature to be seen in many places along the coast.

This feature is even more clearly illustrated in Figure 268, a photograph taken about 5 miles to the north, embracing the whole lower slope of the Andes. The curving of the sand pattern is especially notable as it follows the trends of the valleys in the background. In the foreground, the sand drifts up and over mountains more than a thousand feet high. All the sand comes from the seashore and must be drifting at least 12 or 15 miles inland.

About 15 miles beyond Casma (9°20′ S.), on the border of the irrigated valley of the Río Nepeña, the street pattern of a ruined village is recognizable a little below the center of Figure 269. The photograph was taken with the thought that the ruins were those of an Inca town, but subsequent inquiry indicates that they are much older, probably Mochica.[3] In addition to the ruins, the photograph shows a typical irrigated valley, with sugar plantations at the extreme left, the braided channel of the stream, and the absolutely barren desert outside the irrigated area.

Certain features of the coast line in this part of Peru raise some physiographic problems. Rugged offshore islands and rocky peninsulas such as the Península de Ferrol (1500 feet), ten miles south of Chimbote [270], suggest sinking of the land and the submergence of isolated small moun-

---

[3] In response to a letter of inquiry enclosing a copy of the photograph, Mr. F. Krarup, manager of near-by Hacienda San Jacinto, writes: "The ruins . . . go under the name of Michin. . . . The state of the ruins and their archaeological style suggest some pre-Incaic period. The walls are built of rough hewn stone and cemented with mud, and the whole construction is of primitive design." In his book, "Los Mochicas" (Vol. 1, Lima, 1938), Rafael Larco Hoyle shows "Michán" as one of several pueblos in the Río Nepeña valley.

tain ranges such as characterize the Andean foothill belt in this region. The recency of submergence is suggested by the lack of noticeable wave planation on the peninsula.[4] In striking contrast with this is the appearance of the mainland as shown in Figure 271, looking eastward only 2½ miles farther north, where a smoothly beveled terrace, evidently planed by the waves, truncates steeply dipping rocks.

For many miles along the coast—south for at least 45 miles (see Figure 267) and north for at least 80 miles to Trujillo—such stripped plains were noted along the shore, in some localities extending for at least 2 or 3 miles inland. In many places they are backed by distinct wave-cut cliffs [272]; elsewhere, cliffs are not recognizable and the inner margins of these plains grade into old-age surfaces in such a way as to suggest that preëxisting pediments may locally have been stripped by the waves in their lower parts. Whether wave-cut or pedimented, this stripped coastal plain testifies to a long stand of the land not far below its present elevation with respect to sea level. In contrast, the shore features of the peninsula [270] indicate recent sinking. The physiographic evidence, therefore, strongly suggests that a fault exists between the mainland and the peninsula and that relatively recent movement along it has dropped the peninsula while the mainland has been slightly elevated.

On the beveled terrace shown in Figure 271 drifting sand has built two perfect compound crescent dunes, or barchans, and several smaller ones, some of which string out from the horn of the crescent of one of the larger dunes. What is probably one of the pre-Inca walls of the type found by the Shippee-Johnson expedition about 18 miles farther north[5] crosses the picture somewhat above the center.

Most of the characteristic features of the foothill belt in this part of Peru are combined in Figure 272, looking northeast across Cerro Chao (1611 feet) from a point over the coast 38 miles south-southeast of Trujillo. In the foreground is a sand-covered wave-cut plain backed by a distinct wave-cut cliff partly buried under sand. Beyond, a sand-veneered pediment rises steeply toward Cerro Chao, and in the back-

---

[4] For other photographs of this part of the Peruvian coast see George R. Johnson: Peru from the Air, with text and notes by Raye R. Platt, *Amer. Geogr. Soc. Special Publ. No. 12*, 1930.

[5] Robert Shippee: The "Great Wall of Peru" and Other Aerial Photographic Studies by the Shippee-Johnson Peruvian Expedition, *Geogr. Rev.*, Vol. 22, 1932, pp. 1–29.

ground are broad old-age pedimented valleys and residual mountain groups. Seven miles farther on, at the north end of the same small mountain range, Figure 273 shows the characteristic giant current ripples in the sand blowing up and over the range. The sand, which is entirely derived from the beach, travels inland at least 10 to 15 miles over all obstacles in its path. The rocks in this region are mainly metamorphic and intrusive, though a few miles farther south large masses of ancient lavas as well as sedimentary rocks are involved in the mountain structures.

The finest crescent sand dune seen along the Peruvian coast, and probably one of the largest and finest in the world, lies about 4 miles inland, 2 or 3 miles north of the irrigated valley of the Río Virú and about 22 miles south-southeast of Trujillo [274]. It is a compound barchan with smaller barchans strung out from each horn of the crescent. Its size may be judged from the mule trail in the foreground and from the modern highway crossing the picture in the background. It lies on a sand-swept plain like those previously described. In the extreme lower right are what may be the remains of a pre-Inca defense wall such as are common in this part of Peru.[6]

The irrigated land in northern Peru is devoted largely to the culture of sugar cane under a system of large plantations. Figure 275, looking toward the Andes up the valley of the Río Moche from a point 3 or 4 miles above Trujillo, affords a close-up view of a typical valley utilized in this manner. In the center is a sugar mill and its tributary village, and at the lower right one of the mounds or *huacas* built by the pre-Inca inhabitants of the region, who, as thoroughly as the moderns, appreciated and utilized the opportunities for irrigation afforded by such a mountain stream as the Moche.

Every valley in northern Peru in which the stream carries sufficient water is irrigated. Nearly every valley supports a town, the size of which is commonly roughly proportionate to the area of irrigable land. Commonly each valley is served by its own port on the coast. This is necessary because of the lack of adequate land transportation from valley to valley.

---

[6] *ibid.*

Trujillo to Talara

Between Trujillo and Talara, near the western extremity of South America, we followed a nearly straight course about N. 33°W. to Paita, and thence northward to Talara. Within 10 miles of Trujillo the coastal lowland begins to widen toward the north as the Andes maintain a nearly straight front trending about N. 26°W. and the coast line swings to the west. The coastal plain reaches a maximum width of 65 miles between the promontory of Cerro Illesca and the Andes. In its southern part, where five good-sized streams draining a high and extensive portion of the Andean highland furnish sufficient water, this plain is intensively irrigated, but in its widest part, in northern Lambayeque and southern Piura departments, most of the Sechura Desert is unreclaimed inasmuch as adequate water can be obtained only by tunneling the Andes and diverting headwater tributaries of the Río Marañón.[7]

The broader aspects of the physiography of the coastal region between Trujillo and the first of the irrigated valleys (Chicama) to the north are portrayed in Figure 276, looking northward from the old port of Huanchaco. A low and narrow elevated marine terrace is backed by an abandoned wave-cut cliff, which truncates a broad combined alluvial fan and pediment sloping down from the foothill ranges of igneous and metamorphic rocks visible in the background. The group of boys riding the surf astride tiny balsas—canoe rafts made of dried reeds—provides a reminder of ancient times.

A few moments after the take-off from Trujillo our plane passed over the remarkable ruins of the large pre-Inca city of Chan-Chan, lying close to the sea near the lower margin of the alluvial slope mentioned above. The size and plan of these ruins are suggested by Figure 277, but the interested reader is urged to consult the much better photographs and descriptions previously published by the American Geographical Society.[8] Rectangular enclosures, some of which have dimensions of 1000 to 1300 feet to a side, seem to have constituted complete units,

---

[7] See "Irrigation Projects in Peru," *Geogr. Rev.*, Vol. 17, 1927, pp. 487–490 (with map).

[8] Otto Holstein: Chan-Chan: Capital of the Great Chimu, *Geogr. Rev.*, Vol. 17, 1927, pp. 36–61; George R. Johnson, *op. cit.*, pp. 11–14.

including plazas, apartments, storehouses, and, typically, a large rectangular pit (black area at the lower left) dug down to ground water
(20 to 30 feet) to assure an independent water supply.

For more than 200 miles north of Trujillo the Andean front presents
a rather uniform aspect, typified by Figure 278, looking east from a
point 4 miles north of San Pedro de Lloc and an equal distance east of
the port of Pacasmayo. West of the main range are many small residual
mountain masses, composed of intrusive and metamorphic rocks and
ancient lavas of complex structure, bordered by pediments and fans,
and separated from each other by broad lowlands. Although generally
on a smaller scale, the major features of the foothill belt are similar to
those of the desert ranges and basins of southern Arizona and Nevada.
Of the lowlands between and around the foothill ranges, only the parts
on or adjacent to the fans of the larger mountain streams have been successfully irrigated.

In the vicinity of Chiclayo, as well as farther north, the coastal lowland widens greatly and the foothill ranges in the region near the coast
appear only as small rocky islands protruding above a vast alluvial plain.
This feature is illustrated in Figure 279, looking east from a point about
5½ miles northwest of Chiclayo, which appears a short distance to the
right of the center. Three of these rocky protuberances can be seen beyond the city, and another low one forms the light area below the right
center. The plain gives the impression of having been formed by sinking
and aggradation rather than by uplift and planation, as is the case farther
south between Casma and Trujillo.

To the north, beyond the irrigated area, an arid plain (the Sechura
Desert) with a width in the central part of 50 to 65 miles extends for 90
miles along our course. The general features of this region are faithfully
portrayed in the foreground and middle distance of Figure 280, looking
east 15 miles beyond Chiclayo. The desert is covered by a very sparse
growth of low shrubs except around the branching ends of the dry
drainage channels leading out from the mountains, where a denser
growth of larger shrubby trees occurs. Tiny barchans (not visible in
this picture) scattered widely over the plain testify to a prevailing wind
from the south. In the region east of Bahía de Sechura much larger
quantities of sand have accumulated, locally forming very large dunes.

Many large shallow lakes, probably blocked by coastal sand bars, occur in this area.

At the northern end of the Sechura Desert, in the neighborhood of Piura, a considerable area has been irrigated by the waters of the Río Piura. Looking east from a position about 20 miles below Piura [281], we see the river and part of the irrigated area in the foreground and, beyond, the desert with several of the shallow lakes (darker areas) already mentioned.

Somewhere between Chiclayo and Paita (5°5′ S.) the subsidence inferred at the former city has changed to recent uplift, so that the plain east and north of Paita—the well known *tablazo* of the oil-fields region of northern Peru [282]—was formed by the waves of a Pleistocene sea beveling far inland across tilted and faulted weak Tertiary sedimentary rocks, making a broad, wave-cut platform.[9] The wave-cut terrace so formed, veneered with a few tens of feet of Pleistocene wave-worked gravels, sands, and shell beds, has since been broadly warped and uplifted in amounts ranging from almost nothing at the south to two or three hundred feet at Paita and as much as 1100 feet near Cabo Blanco about 55 miles farther north. The tablazo in the Talara region is 15 to 20 miles wide.

In Figure 282 we are looking west to the ocean from a point about 4 miles east of Paita, which, with numerous small boats lying at anchor in the harbor, can be seen below the cliffs at the head of the nearer bay. Streams are beginning to cut back into the tablazo, but most of its surface is unmodified. In the foreground the curving patterns of the old strand lines, formed as the tablazo was being elevated, can still be seen.

About 5 miles north of Paita our course lay a short distance out to sea, affording an opportunity to photograph the high wave-cut cliff along the eastern side of Bahía de Paita in its relation to the smooth surface of the tablazo in the background [283]. In front of the cliff are a lagoon and an offshore sand bar formed by prograding sediments brought to the sea a short distance north by the Río Chira.

Looking northwest from a position about 13 miles along the route beyond Paita, we see a remarkable display of strand lines converging at

---

[9] See Arthur Iddings and A. A. Olsson: Geology of Northwest Peru, *Bull. Amer. Assn. of Petroleum Geologists*, Vol. 12, 1928, pp. 1–39.

the westernmost point in continental South America, Punta Pariñas [284]. The strand lines are close to sea level and are covered in part during high tides. They have been formed by prograding of the shore line by sediment carried northward from the Río Chira.

A few minutes after this picture was taken, we passed over some of Peru's most productive oil fields, on the tablazo south and east of Talara, and landed at the Talara airport on this upland between canyons reminiscent of the Dakota badlands. The principal oil fields of Peru, and for that matter of the entire Pacific slope of South America, are found in the Talara region.

258. The even crest of the Andean front range near Nazca (ESE, from ca. 14°50′ S., 74°52′ W.). Note the large mass of drifted sand on the mountain spur at the right

259. The curiously marked surface of an alluvial plain near Nazca (NE, from ca. 14°39′ S., 74°59′ W.)

260. An irrigated valley at the foot of the Andes, about 28 miles northwest of Nazca (NE, from ca. 14°35′ S., 75°3′ W.)

261. Looking seaward across the irrigated valley of the Río de Ica from a point about 22 miles southeast of Ica (SW, from ca. 14°19′ S., 75°29′ W.)

262. The western slope of the Andes near Ica (E, from ca. 14°10′ S., 75°38′ W.)

263. The western front of the Andes and the irrigated plain of the Río de Lurin, as seen from the ancient citadel of Pachacamac, about 15 miles southeast of Lima (E, from 12°14′ S., 76°57′ W.)

264. The western front of the Andes, as seen from a position about 68 miles north-northwest of the Lima airport (ENE, from 11°15′ S., 77°29′ W.)

265. Sugar plantations in a typical irrigated valley, probably that of the Río de la Fortaleza (NE, from 10°38′ S., 77°49′ W.)

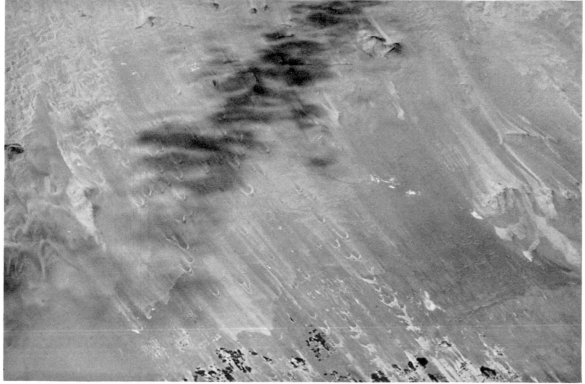

266.	The intricately dissected western slope of the Andes rising gradually eastward from the sea (ENE, from 10°22′ S., 77°58′ W.)

267.	Sand drifting inland across a rocky and presumably wave-cut plain northwest of Casma (ENE, from 9°26′ S., 78°24′ W.)

268. Sand driven far inland by prevailing southwesterly winds, about 10 miles northwest of Casma (NE, from 9°22′ S., 78°25′ W.)

269. The irrigated Río Nepeña valley, about midway between Casma and Chimbote (E, from 9°17′ S., 78°28′ W.). Note the ruins of a pre-Inca town on the margin of the cultivated land

270. The rocky Península de Ferrol, the coast line of which suggests recent land subsidence, as seen from a position 9 miles south-southeast of Chimbote (W, from 9°10′ S., 78°30′ W.)

271. Crescent sand dunes on a rocky coastal platform 7 miles southeast of Chimbote (E, from 9°8′ S., 78°31′ W.)

272. Sand drifting far inland over an abandoned wave-cut cliff and the mountains beyond, about 38 miles south-southeast of Trujillo (NE, from 8°36′ S., 78°46′ W.)

273. Waves of drifting sand burying a mountain range south of the Río Virú (NE, from 8°30' S., 78°49' W.)

274. A great compound crescent sand dune 22 miles south-southeast of Trujillo (NE, from ca. 8°24' S., 78°52' W.). The scale is indicated by the highway near the top of the picture

275. Sugar plantations in the valley of the Río Moche a few miles above Trujillo (E, from 8°6′ S., 79°0′ W.)

276. Surf riders in balsa canoes at the old port of Huanchaco, along a coast typical of the region north of Trujillo (N, from 8°5′ S., 79°8′ W.)

277. A portion of the ruins of the pre-Inca city of Chan-Chan north of Trujillo (ENE, from 8°5' S., 79°4' W.)

278. A view typical of the Andean front between Trujillo and Chiclayo, as seen from a point 4 miles east of Pacasmayo (E, from 7°23' S., 79°31' W.)

279. Chiclayo and its surroundings (E, from 6°45′ S., 79°55′ W.)

280. Scattered clumps of low brush dot the arid plain of the Sechura Desert, 15 miles northwest of Chiclayo (E, from 6°37′ S., 80°1′ W.)

281. Shallow lakes in the Sechura Desert, as seen from a point over the irrigated Río Piura plain 33 miles southeast of Paita (E, from 5°28′ S., 80°48′ W.)

282. The city of Paita and a portion of the elevated wave-cut terrace or tablazo characteristic of this part of Peru (W, from 5°4′ S., 81°4′ W.)

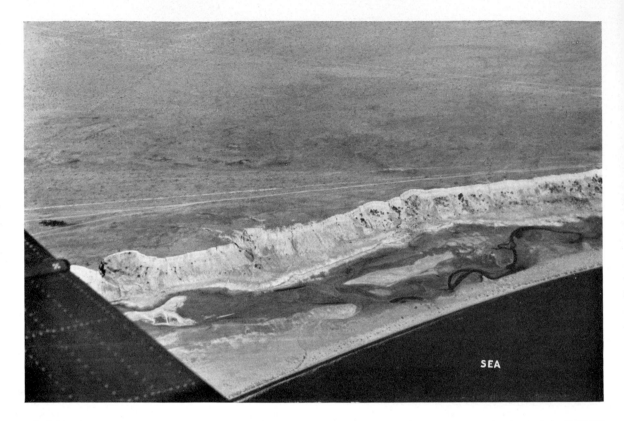

SEA

283. A high wave-cut cliff bordering the tablazo about 5 miles north of Paita (E, from 5°0′ S., 81°6′ W.)

284. Strand lines south of Punta Pariñas, the westernmost point in continental South America (N, from 4°52′ S., 81°8′ W.)

ECUADOR*

Talara to Quito

FROM Talara we followed a nearly direct line about N. 30°E. to Guayaquil, and thence about N. 25°E. over the lowland plains along the Río Vinces and its continuation, the Río Palenque, to approximately latitude 0°35′ S., where we turned east-northeast across the mountains to the Quito basin. Ten to fifteen miles north of Talara, where the tablazo approaches an elevation of 1000 feet, is a notable display of the phenomena of headward erosion on a youthful plain. Each valley heads in a dry waterfall where the wet-weather stream plunges over the relatively resistant veneer of wave-deposited gravels capping the tablazo, and each is guided in its headward recession by slight inherited irregularities of the tablazo surface similar to those noted in Figure 282 near Paita. Unfortunately, a dawn flight from Talara prevented the taking of a photographic record of these distinctive physiographic phenomena.

The tablazo becomes more and more dissected as its elevation increases toward the north, until, finally, little of it is left near the coast. A few miles south of Tumbes (latitude 3°35′ S.) the higher land swings eastward away from the coast and our route passed diagonally out from shore across the Gulf of Guayaquil, so that between Tumbes and Machala only a wide, low alluvial plain [291] could be definitely recognized in front of the distant Andes. In this picture we are looking southeast across the delta of the Río Zarumilla. Low hills can be detected rising from the plain far in front of the Andes, which, in this region, are somewhat broken and not so high as farther south. The western front of the upland is about 40 miles away, and the peaks on the sky line nearly 80.

At about 6.50 on the morning of our flight, the northern part of the Gulf of Guayaquil was covered by a flat-topped mass of stratus clouds from which, here and there, cumulus thunderheads were beginning to rise [285]. These were very beautiful in the morning sun, especially when they had risen to still greater heights.

After passing Isla de Puná, concealed from view, we came down below the clouds in time to see the tip of the Río Guayas delta [286]. We are looking about S. 52°E. across the tree-lined outer distributaries of

* See Map VII, p. 287, below.

the delta. Patterns indicating a rapid forward building of the delta are readily recognized opposite the mouths of the eastern distributaries.

From Guayaquil we at first flew northward close to the Río Guayas. Looking northwest from a point about 7 miles northeast of Guayaquil [287], we see the river flowing in what appears to be a slightly entrenched course across a plain, above which low, wooded hills rise beyond the river. The lowlands are grassy, and those in the foreground, although they show shallow watercourses, seem to be above the flood plain.

Looking steeply down toward the south-southeast, 9 miles northeast of Guayaquil [288], we see an entrenched plain on which the drainage pattern is suggestive of a tidal marsh. If it is such a marsh, extremely high tides are indicated, because the area is drained by a trench of considerable depth. Several buildings can be seen along the bank of the Río Guayas in the left foreground.

Most of the essential geographic features of the plain north of Guayaquil are shown in Figure 289, taken 24 miles N. 21° E. of the city, looking west across the lower course of the Río de la Bocana and the northern end of Cerro Zamborondón, one of several groups of small hills that rise like islands out of the plain. The hills are forested, but the plain is a grassland with scattered trees. Small lakes of irregular pattern (dark in the picture) can be seen in the left half of the photograph. Flowing toward the observer, to the right of the center, is the Río de la Bocana, which evidently serves as the only means of communication in the region, since houses are scattered at short intervals along its banks and no roads are visible.

For the next 27 miles to the north, the plain and its cultural imprint remained essentially the same as in the preceding picture. The streams seem to furnish the only means of communication. The crops noted were corn, sugar, bananas, and small orchards of a large, dark-green tree, possibly orange or mango. Toward the north the proportion of forest gradually increases.

After passing over a belt of clouds for about 25 miles, we again obtained a view westward over the plain from a point a short distance east of the Río Palenque and about 78 miles along the course from Guayaquil [290]. The plain here appears to be gently rolling and mostly forested, and little evidence of human occupation was visible from a height of 10,000 feet.

Because of clouds, nothing more was seen of this plain west of the Andes. As we turned eastward to cross the western rim of the Andean upland,[1] two photographs were made of its western front: Figure 292, looking northeast, and Figure 294, looking a little west of south. Clouds obscure the lower slopes, but enough can be seen to indicate that the western border of the upland rises rather abruptly at the front, and then much more gradually to a relatively even sky line. This profile is clearly illustrated in the view to the south. At the extreme left, on the summit between the spurs, are remnants of a relatively flat upland (clearly shown in a photographic panorama extending to the left of Figure 294) in process of active dissection by streams working eastward. Full maturity has been reached along the front, but much of the old-age paramo surface remains near the rim of the upland.

Thus the Andes here have the character of an old-age surface, steeply warped or faulted upward along the front and now in the process of stream dissection. The resulting topography is extremely rugged and is of a type produced by stream erosion on rocks of relatively uniform texture, without strong control either by variations in rock resistance or by relatively recent crustal movements. The rocks, where definitely ob-

---

[1] The Andes of Ecuador are commonly described as consisting of two more or less parallel ranges, known as the Cordillera Oriental and the Cordillera Occidental, with a depression or trough between them which is divided by cross ranges into a number of separate basins. As long ago as 1913, A. C. Veatch (Quito to Bogotá, New York, 1917) recognized the fact that this simple statement did not provide a satisfactory portrayal of the facts. In discussing the broad physiographic nature of the Andes in Ecuador, he says: "These snow-capped mountains (referring to the volcanoes) are the culminating points in the great broad single mountain mass which here forms the Andes. Its top is from 20 to 40 miles wide and the parallel rims are generally called the 'Eastern Cordillera' and the 'Western Cordillera' respectively. Cross-ranges divide the top into a number of great elevated basins or mountain-parks which have a mean elevation of 7,500 to 9,000 feet, while their bordering rims have average heights of 11,000 to 12,000. These high basins are drained by rivers flowing through the ramparts, in some cases to the west into the Pacific, and in others to the east into the Amazon and the Atlantic" (p. 24). Again, he notes that "the conception of the Andes of Ecuador as a double chain requires modification in the sense of considering it rather as a single chain in whose complex top these mountain-parks are situated" (p. 53).

The observations of the writer, based upon a brief visit to Ecuador and a careful study of his aerial photographs, which cover most of the western upland, are in harmony with the earlier views of Veatch. He gained an impression of a plateaulike upland, downfaulted in the center and modified greatly by volcanic masses piled up locally both on the margins of the upland and in and along the borders of the basins.

served [293], appeared to be granitic, and the topography all along the western edge of the Andes in this region is characteristic of granite or of metamorphic rocks such as gneisses of uniform texture. A dense tropical forest testifies to the great increase in rainfall as we have come northward from the Peruvian border.

Only from personal observation or from a stereoscopic picture is it possible to gain a full appreciation of the extreme ruggedness of this dissected front of the Andean upland. In the stereoscopic print [293], we are looking steeply down toward the south into one of the eastern tributaries of the Río Toachi, 31 miles S. 49° W. of Quito. The stream flows out of the valley through a narrow cleft somewhere in the left foreground. Those interested in uncommon landforms are invited to attempt an explanation of the steep-walled amphitheaters on the ridge crests of sloping spurs such as that beginning under the near side of the largest cloud.

Turning to the opposite side of the plane and looking northwest [295], we see on the northeast-facing wall of the Toachi Valley an example of native mountain agriculture utilizing the principle of strip cropping now being advocated by the United States Soil Conservation Service as a means of reducing the ravages of soil erosion. The picture also gives a clear impression of the broader aspects of topography and vegetation in the region and of the difficult and inaccessible terrain in which native agriculture is practiced.

A real thrill awaits the air traveler when, after flying northward from Guayaquil along the rugged, forested, and almost uninhabited western slope of the Andes and northeastward for about 30 miles across the western rim of the upland over scenery such as that shown in the preceding pictures, he crosses the inconspicuous Corazón Pass and suddenly finds below him the Quito basin, an intensively cultivated open country with irregular, hedge-bordered fields, golden with harvest, and numerous groves of blue-green eucalyptus trees. Figure 296, looking about N. 63° W. from a point 8 miles south of Quito, lacks only color to convey the beauty of the basin. Favorable relief, adequate rainfall, a fertile soil of volcanic ash, and an altitude (8000 to 9000 feet) high enough to be healthful combine to endow richly this and other basins of the Ecuadorian Andes.

285. A flat-topped overcast and rising cumulus thunderheads above the Gulf of Guayaquil (W, from ca. 3°6′ S., 80°25′ W.)

286. The southern margin of the Río Guayas delta, about 32 miles south of Guayaquil (ESE, from 2°33′ S., 80°5′ W.)

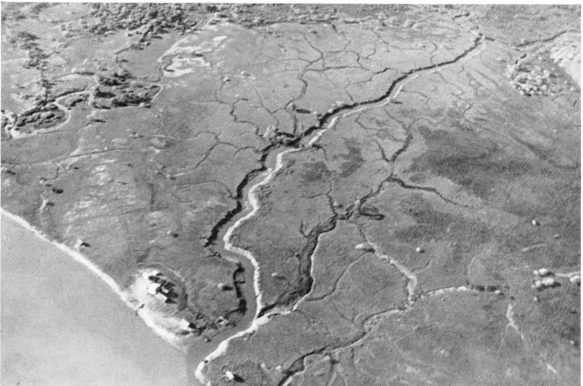

287. The plains bordering the Río Guayas about 7 miles northeast of Guayaquil (WNW, from 2°8′ S., 79°48′ W.)

288. The eastern bank of the Río Guayas 9 miles northeast of Guayaquil (SSE, from 2°6′ S., 79°47′ W.)

289. Plains and low hills characteristic of the area along the Río de la Bocana, 24 miles north-northeast of Guayaquil (W, from 1°54′ S., 79°40′ W.)

290. Forested plains typical of the upper part of the Guayaquil lowland, as seen from a position 78 miles north-northeast of Guayaquil (W, from ca. 1°11′ S., 79°23′ W.)

291–293. (See opposite page)

A NEW REFERENCE MAP

OF

LATIN AMERICA

1:5,000,000

Three large sheets in color

AMERICAN GEOGRAPHICAL SOCIETY

BROADWAY AT 156TH STREET · NEW YORK

1942

MAP OF THE AMERICAS 1:5,000,000

[In three sheets, each 46 x 35 inches: (1) Mexico, Central America, and the West Indies; (2) South America, Sheet North; (3) South America, Sheet South.]

The need is becoming increasingly pressing today for an accurate map of Latin America showing physical features, political boundaries, towns, roads, railroads, airports, etc. in considerable detail and yet on a scale not too large for convenient reference. The American Geographical Society's new map, prepared at the special request of the United States government, is designed to meet this need. It is essentially a revised reduction and simplification of the Society's 107-sheet Map of Hispanic America on the scale of 1:1,000,000, the product of twenty-one years of research.

The northern of the three sheets includes Mexico, Central America, the West Indies, and the Caribbean coast of South America. In addition it covers a large part of the United States, but without the physical

PRICE LIST

I. *Flat paper maps, unmounted:* $2.75 per sheet or $8.25 for set of three sheets

II. *Mounted maps:*	One sheet	*Two sheets of South America mounted together*
1. Mounted on cloth		
a) Rolled with wood rod at top and bottom ready for hanging	$4.50	$ 9.00
b) Dissected and folded to 8½″ x 11″.	5.40	10.80
2. Mounted on map-tack board suitable for use with colored map tacks and map-marking pencils		
a) With taped edges	6.75	14.30
b) Framed* with composition backing	12.50	26.60

The maps are available in two forms: (*a*) base in black, blue, brown, and red, with layer tints (i.e. shades of green and brown showing relief of the land and of blue showing ocean depths); (*b*) base in black, blue, brown, and red, with layer tints omitted (suitable for use as outline maps on which additional data can be plotted).

Educational institutions will receive a discount of 25 per cent on the above prices.

Index (pamphlet) to names on all three sheets: 25 cents.

*Wood frames finished in birch, mahogany, walnut, and golden oak are carried in stock, or frames can be supplied finished to match your trim at no extra cost. Please specify finish desired. Board-mounted maps of this size that are not framed cannot be guaranteed against excessive warping.

detail shown south of the Rio Grande. South America is represented on two sheets, which can be mounted together if desired.

For the first time on a map of Latin America of a comparable scale, relief is shown in detail. This is accomplished by means of form lines and a series of shades of green and brown ascending to the regions of permanent snow, which appear in white. The topography of the ocean bottom is similarly shown by form lines and a series of shades of blue. Water is in blue, and rivers are distinguished as perennial or intermittent, surveyed or unsurveyed. Appropriate symbols indicate important waterfalls, swamps, glaciers, and other features of the physical landscape.

International boundaries have been differentiated as demarcated, undemarcated, or still in dispute. If they are still in dispute, claims of different countries are indicated. Both national boundaries and boundaries of major civil subdivisions are outlined by bands of green. The sovereignty of European possessions and their administrative organization are also shown. Towns are classified as to both administrative importance and population, according to latest available statistics.

Railroads in operation appear in black. Roads reported passable by automobile at most times of the year, as well as important government road projects either under construction or planned, are shown in red. The Pan-American Highway is given a special series of symbols showing the status of the road—whether passable at all times of the year, in the dry season only, or projected. A large selection of airports, landing fields, and important seaplane anchorages are symbolized in red.

All three sheets of the map have been prepared on a new oblique conic conformal projection specially designed and computed for this map and taking into consideration the northwest-southeast trend of the Americas. On each sheet is a text explaining how to make linear and areal measurements. By following the method described, distances can be readily measured, with errors of less than 1 per cent.

AMERICAN GEOGRAPHICAL SOCIETY
BROADWAY AT 156TH STREET, NEW YORK CITY

Please fill the following order for the Map of the Americas, 1:5,000,000 with[out] index. I enclose $_____ in payment. [See price list on adjoining page.]

	a) With layer tints		b) Without layer tints	
	Quantity	Price	Quantity	Price
Flat paper maps, unmounted				
Price: $2.75 per sheet —$8.25 per set				
(1) Mexico, Central America, and Caribbean sheet				
(2) South America, Sheet North				
(3) South America, Sheet South				
Maps mounted on cloth or tack board				
(1) Mexico, Central America, and Caribbean sheet				
(2) South America, Sheet North				
(3) South America, Sheet South				
(2) and (3) South America, Sheets North and South together				

[If index is desired, please indicate quantity (   ) and price (   ).]

[If mounted maps are desired, please give instructions below as to type of mounting desired.]

_____

_____

NAME_____

ADDRESS_____

_____

THE FACE
OF SOUTH AMERICA

An Aerial Traverse

by JOHN LYON RICH

AMERICAN GEOGRAPHICAL SOCIETY

Broadway at 156th Street

NEW YORK

1942

THIS BOOK presents a panorama of South America as the traveler sees it from the air. Plantations on the Guiana coastal plains; broad estuaries of the Amazon delta with their winding channels and forested islands; savannas and brushlands of the Brazilian "drought region"; coffee uplands of southeastern Brazil; open pampas of the Argentine; barren slopes and crags of the Andes; blistering nitrate deserts of Chile; bold headlands of the Peruvian coast; the mountain-rimmed basins of Quito and Bogotá —these and much more besides are laid out before the reader.

In 1939 Dr. Rich, who is a professor of geology at the University of Cincinnati, made a flight by commercial airways around South America (see map on preceding page). En route he took more than 900 photographs from the air, about a third of which, together with a few ground views, are reproduced in this volume. The text interprets in detail the land and water forms, the aspects of the vegetation, and the works of man appearing in the pictures.

Photographs and text provide a background for a better understanding of many of South America's contemporary problems— problems in the use of the land, in the development of transportation systems and mineral resources, in the conquest of poverty and disease. These problems "do not present themselves with their full impact to the casual traveler who spends a few days in the principal cities. . . . The cities, like the flowers of a plant, depend on what is behind them for life and nourishment. They may be beautiful, and, as in the case of some capitals, they may be even more elaborate than the resources surrounding them properly warrant, but they are, after all, nourished by the country surrounding them. It is this countryside that the air traveler is able to see to better advantage than others."

"The Face of South America" is particularly recommended for supplementary reading and study in college courses in general geography or in the geography or economics of South America. Route maps on the scale of 1:5,000,000 show where each picture was taken and the direction in which the camera was pointed. The subject references in the index have been prepared with fullness and care in order to enable those interested in physiographic, geological, or vegetational features, or in human uses and modifications of the natural environment, conveniently to find pictures showing characteristic examples.

"The Face of South America" constitutes *American Geographical Society Special Publication* No. 26, xviii and 301 pages; 325 half-tones and 8 maps

---

AMERICAN GEOGRAPHICAL SOCIETY
BROADWAY AT 156TH STREET
NEW YORK, N. Y.

Gentlemen:

Please send a copy of "The Face of South America" to the following address. I enclose check for $4.00 in payment.

Name ....

Address ....

....

If you wish at the same time to order other publications of the Society from the list on the back of this page, please indicate the titles below and enclose payment.

....

....

....

AMERICAN GEOGRAPHICAL SOCIETY

PUBLICATIONS

A Selected List

THE GEOGRAPHICAL REVIEW. A quarterly periodical containing articles, notes, and book reviews, fully illustrated with photographs and maps. $5.00 a year.

FOCUS ON AFRICA. By Richard Upjohn Light, photographs by Mary Light. 224 pp., aerial photographs, maps. 1941. $5.00.

MAP OF THE AMERICAS: 1:5,000,000. 3 large sheets in color: 1) Mexico, Central America, and the West Indies; 2) South America, Sheet North; 3) South America, Sheet South. 1942. $2.75 per sheet.

MAP OF HISPANIC AMERICA: 1:1,000,000, in 107 sheets, of which 101 have been published. Compiled and reproduced in conformity with the "International Map of the World on the Scale of 1:1,000,000." $2.00 per sheet.

CHILE: LAND AND SOCIETY. By George McCutchen McBride. 408 pp.; maps and photographs. 1936. $4.00.

PERU FROM THE AIR. By George R. Johnson. 159 pp.; aerial photographs. 1930. $3.50.

THE DISCOVERY OF THE AMAZON, According to the Account of Friar Gaspar de Carvajal and Other Documents. By José Toribio Medina, translated by Bertram E. Lee, edited by H. C. Heaton. 481 pp. 1934. $4.00.

THE EUROPEAN POSSESSIONS IN THE CARIBBEAN AREA. A Compilation of Facts Concerning their Population, Physical Geography, Resources, Industries, Trade, Government, and Strategic Importance. 116 pp.; insert map in 3 colors. 1941. $1.00.

ENVIRONMENT AND CONFLICT IN EUROPE. Four basic maps and 14 special maps; printed in colors on a single sheet (35 x 45 inches), with accompanying booklet. 2nd ed. rev., 1940. $1.00.

WHITE SETTLERS IN THE TROPICS. By Dr. A. Grenfell Price, Master of St. Mark's College, University of Adelaide, South Australia. 311 pp.; maps, diagrams, and photographs. 1939. $4.00.

INNER ASIAN FRONTIERS OF CHINA. By Owen Lattimore, Director of the Page School of International Relations, The Johns Hopkins University; Editor of *Pacific Affairs.* 585 pp.; maps. 1940. $4.00.

THE FACE
OF SOUTH AMERICA

An Aerial Traverse

by JOHN LYON RICH

AMERICAN GEOGRAPHICAL SOCIETY

Broadway at 156th Street

NEW YORK

1942

THIS BOOK presents a panorama of South America as the traveler sees it from the air. Plantations on the Guiana coastal plains; broad estuaries of the Amazon delta with their winding channels and forested islands; savannas and brushlands of the Brazilian "drought region"; coffee uplands of southeastern Brazil; open pampas of the Argentine; barren slopes and crags of the Andes; blistering nitrate deserts of Chile; bold headlands of the Peruvian coast; the mountain-rimmed basins of Quito and Bogotá —these and much more besides are laid out before the reader.

In 1939 Dr. Rich, who is a professor of geology at the University of Cincinnati, made a flight by commercial airways around South America (see map on preceding page). En route he took more than 900 photographs from the air, about a third of which, together with a few ground views, are reproduced in this volume. The text interprets in detail the land and water forms, the aspects of the vegetation, and the works of man appearing in the pictures.

Photographs and text provide a background for a better understanding of many of South America's contemporary problems— problems in the use of the land, in the development of transportation systems and mineral resources, in the conquest of poverty and disease. These problems "do not present themselves with their full impact to the casual traveler who spends a few days in the principal cities. . . . The cities, like the flowers of a plant, depend on what is behind them for life and nourishment. They may be beautiful, and, as in the case of some capitals, they may be even more elaborate than the resources surrounding them properly warrant, but they are, after all, nourished by the country surrounding them. It is this countryside that the air traveler is able to see to better advantage than others."

"The Face of South America" is particularly recommended for supplementary reading and study in college courses in general geography or in the geography or economics of South America. Route maps on the scale of 1:5,000,000 show where each picture was taken and the direction in which the camera was pointed. The subject references in the index have been prepared with fullness and care in order to enable those interested in physiographic, geological, or vegetational features, or in human uses and modifications of the natural environment, conveniently to find pictures showing characteristic examples.

"The Face of South America" constitutes *American Geographical Society Special Publication* No. 26, xviii and 301 pages; 325 half-tones and 8 maps

---

AMERICAN GEOGRAPHICAL SOCIETY
BROADWAY AT 156TH STREET
NEW YORK, N. Y.

25% DISCOUNT TO FELLOWS

Gentlemen:

Please send a copy of "The Face of South America" to the following address. I enclose check for $4.00 in payment.

    Name ....

    Address ....

....

If you wish at the same time to order other publications of the Society from the list on the back of this page, please indicate the titles below and enclose payment.

....

....

....

AMERICAN GEOGRAPHICAL SOCIETY

PUBLICATIONS

A Selected List

THE GEOGRAPHICAL REVIEW. A quarterly periodical containing articles, notes, and book reviews, fully illustrated with photographs and maps. $5.00 a year.

FOCUS ON AFRICA. By Richard Upjohn Light, photographs by Mary Light. 224 pp., aerial photographs, maps. 1941. $5.00.

MAP OF THE AMERICAS: 1:5,000,000. 3 large sheets in color: 1) Mexico, Central America, and the West Indies; 2) South America, Sheet North; 3) South America, Sheet South. 1942 $2.75 per sheet.

MAP OF HISPANIC AMERICA: 1:1,000,000, in 107 sheets, of which 101 have been published. Compiled and reproduced in conformity with the "International Map of the World on the Scale of 1:1,000,000." $2.00 per sheet.

CHILE: LAND AND SOCIETY. By George McCutchen McBride. 408 pp.; maps and photographs. 1936. $4.00.

PERU FROM THE AIR. By George R. Johnson. 159 pp.; aerial photographs. 1930. $3.50.

THE DISCOVERY OF THE AMAZON, According to the Account of Friar Gaspar de Carvajal and Other Documents. By José Toribio Medina, translated by Bertram E. Lee, edited by H. C. Heaton. 481 pp. 1934. $4.00.

THE EUROPEAN POSSESSIONS IN THE CARIBBEAN AREA. A Compilation of Facts Concerning their Population, Physical Geography, Resources, Industries, Trade, Government, and Strategic Importance. 116 pp.; insert map in 3 colors. 1941. $1.00.

ENVIRONMENT AND CONFLICT IN EUROPE. Four basic maps and 14 special maps; printed in colors on a single sheet (35 x 45 inches), with accompanying booklet. 2nd ed. rev., 1940. $1.00.

WHITE SETTLERS IN THE TROPICS. By Dr. A. Grenfell Price, Master of St. Mark's College, University of Adelaide, South Australia. 311 pp.; maps, diagrams, and photographs. 1939. $4.00.

INNER ASIAN FRONTIERS OF CHINA. By Owen Lattimore, Director of the Page School of International Relations, The Johns Hopkins University; Editor of *Pacific Affairs.* 585 pp.; maps. 1940. $4.00.

Owing to an error, the two pictures forming Figure 293 on page 246 are transposed. For the use of readers who may wish to view them in a stereoscope they are reproduced below in their proper positions.

After the long flight over the coastal deserts of Chile and Peru the green beauty of the Quito region is very welcome. Thanks to a fertile and easily tilled volcanic soil and generally adequate rainfall, the people of this region, a large proportion of whom are Indian, do not have to face the great natural handicaps that oppose the mountain dwellers in the drier high Andes farther south.

In Figure 297 we have a glimpse of a typical Ecuadorian village not far from Quito. The houses have a distinctive design not seen elsewhere in South America. At the front of the house (on the left) is an open porch under the main roof, separated from the street by a stone wall about 3 feet high, into which is built the cooking stove. Meat or other items for sale are often hung from cords stretched between the wood pillars on which rests the beam supporting the roof at the front of the porch. Various details of house construction are revealed at the right; bamboo plastered and daubed with mud is extensively used.

The Ecuadorian landscape is beautiful, from the ground as well as from the air, with many colorful flowering trees and a great variety of attractive, but generally spiny, flowering shrubs. Agriculture is not confined to the flatter lands of the basin. In many places the hillsides, even though very steep, are cultivated, as is shown in Figure 298, a photograph taken in the hills about 9 miles north of Quito.

Quito to Río Mira

From Quito the route lay northward down the valley of the Río Guaillabamba to the point where the river turns to the west. Thence, crossing the long westward-projecting spur of the Cordillera de Intac (in the background of Figure 292) at a pass close to the place where it diverges from the main Andean range, we skirted the western sides of the high massives of Cerro Cotacachi and Cerro Yana-Urcu and continued a few miles west of the Andean front to the Río Patía valley in southern Colombia. From there we turned northeastward through a

TITLES TO FIGURES 291–293.

291. The delta of the Río Zarumilla and the western front of the Andes, as seen from a point just off the coast between Tumbes and Machala (SE, from ca. 3°12′ S., 80°28′ W.)
292. The western side of the Andes, about 42 miles southwest of Quito (NNE, from 0°33′ S., 79°0′ W.)
293. A stereoscopic view of the sharply dissected mountains along the western border of the Andean upland about 31 miles southwest of Quito (S, from 0°31′ S., 78°50′ W.)

gap formed by the Patía and over a low divide into the Cauca Valley, a broad structural basin between the western and central chains of the Andes, and followed the Cauca to Cali. Owing to a delay in the receipt of my permit for photography, no photographs were taken over the Colombian part of this route.

The Quito basin east and northeast of Quito [299] is generally similar to that to the southwest [296] except that at the lower elevations, as in the foreground, the climate is considerably more arid. In this photograph, which affords an excellent impression of the setting of the capital city, we are looking southwest from a point over the Río Guaillabamba valley 10 miles from Quito. The city appears as a light area about 1 ¾ inches from the left side of the photograph and 0.8 inch from the top. The lower slopes of an old dissected volcano, Cerro Pichincha, appear in the upper right background, and what has every appearance of being a relatively recent fault scarp crosses the picture from left to right just above the center. The ash-covered slopes in the foreground are intensively cultivated in a pattern of tiny fields. On the lower slopes of Cerro Pichincha are some of the many eucalyptus groves that, under governmental encouragement, have been planted in Ecuador during the past three-quarters of a century and have added much to the wealth of the otherwise treeless Quito basin.

About 16 miles north-northeast of Quito, along the Guaillabamba Valley where the elevation has dropped to 8000 feet, the rainfall is so small that the native vegetation includes agave, cactus, and other xerophytic plants and irrigation is necessary. In Figure 300, looking slightly south of west, we see in the left foreground part of the irrigated land in the Guaillabamba Valley and the dry, almost barren lower slopes of the adjoining mountains. The photograph also includes, at approximately the location marked by the white circle, an impressive stone marker erected on the equator. This monument, shown in the small inset, is one of the few places from which a tourist can carry home a photograph of himself, comfortable in a topcoat, sitting half in the northern hemisphere and half in the southern.

As we approach the pass at the eastern end of the Cordillera de Intac, we find the slopes clothed with a rain forest. Small patches of the flatter ground, and even some of the steep hillsides, have been cleared for agriculture, as is shown in Figure 301, looking west down the valley of a small tributary of the Guaillabamba. Along the line of flight this is the last cleared area of any considerable size to be seen for a distance of about 120 miles to the valley of the Río Patía. In that entire distance only a few small native clearings along some of the streams give indication that man has ever been in the region.

As we flew over this forested jungle parallel to the Andean front, the nature of that front as the edge of an uplifted old-age surface was everywhere apparent [302]. Streams working back have dissected its margin into an intricate maze of hills and valleys, but large areas of the grassy upland paramos retain their old-age features of moderate relief, as can be seen in the upper right part of the picture. On the opposite side of the range in the background (Paramos de Piñan) is one of the larger basins or mountain parks of the Ecuadorian Andes. There, along the north and south highway, are found the city of Ibarra and the larger part of the population in this latitude.

The streams which drain this basin, converging from both north and south, break through the western rim of the upland in the canyon of the Río Mira [303]. In the foreground is the lower, late-mature, densely forested land over which we have flown since crossing the Cordillera de Intac, trenched rather sharply by the Río Mira, as well as by various smaller streams. Beyond, the land rises abruptly to the paramos. The Ibarra basin already mentioned is situated between these high paramos and the eastern rim of the upland (seen under the distant clouds).

294. The western margin of the Andean upland, as seen from a point about 40 miles southwest of Quito (S, from 0°32′ S., 78°58′ W.). Clouds at an elevation of about 5000 feet conceal the base of the mountains

295. Native agriculture on the steep slopes of the Río Toachi valley about 30 miles southwest of Quito (NW, from 0°31′ S., 78°49′ W.)

296. Landscape patterns in the Quito basin 8 miles south of Quito (W, from 0°20′ S., 78°30′ W.)

297. A street in a typical village near Quito

298. Steep mountain slopes under cultivation about 9 miles north of Quito

299. Quito and its surroundings, as seen from a point 10 miles northeast of the city (SW, from 0°7′ S., 78°22′ W.)

300. A view across the valley of the Río Guaillabamba to the northern slopes of Cerro Pichincha (W, from 0°1′ N., 78°22′ W.). The white circle indicates the approximate position of the stone marker erected on the equator (see inset)

301. Mountain agriculture along a rain forest margin about 33 miles north of Quito (W, from ca. 0°16′ N., 78°27′ W.)

302. The sharply dissected western margin of the Andean upland and the paramo above timber line, as seen from a point about 62 miles north of Quito (ESE, from 0°41′ N., 78°23′ W.)

303. A view up the valley of the Río Mira (SE, from 0°54′ N., 78°20′ W.)

304. A forested landscape characteristic of the region lying to the west of the route between the area shown in Figure 301 and the Río Patía in Colombia (W, from 1°6′ N., 78°16′ W.)

COLOMBIA AND PANAMA*

Río Mira to Cali

THE nature of the country along and to the west of our route all the way from the Cordillera de Intac to the Río Patía is typified by Figure 304, looking west-northwest down the river at the Colombian border. The relief is everywhere moderate and in many places is definitely an old-age phase of an earlier cycle beginning to be entrenched by the streams after a relatively recent uplift. Although flowing in meandering courses, the streams are white with foaming rapids, and many small waterfalls were noted. The almost complete lack of structural alignment in the topography leads to the inference that the rocks along the flight line and for 15 to 20 miles to the west are almost homogeneous in composition. As they produce numerous rapids and waterfalls, they are evidently resistant. At only one place, 12 miles beyond the position of this picture, were any structural alignments noted. Here, 6 to 15 miles west of the route, north-south ridges and mesa-like forms were seen. Since these were conspicuous even through the forest cover, it is assumed that if such features had been present elsewhere they would have been noticed.

The Río Patía, in a steep-sided valley similar to that of the Río Mira, but deeper and more rugged, breaks through a gap in the western cordillera (called the Cordillera Occidental in Colombia), on the northern side of which the range seems to be offset *en échelon* about 20 miles to the east. East of the gap, the Patía drains the southern end of the Cauca-Patía trough, a long structural depression 20 to 25 miles wide and trending about N. 21° E. between the western and central Andean ranges. We flew along the western side of the upper course of the Río Patía to an inconspicuous divide within the structural trough, and thence down the Río Cauca to Cali.

After crossing to the eastern side of the Cordillera Occidental we immediately noted a change in vegetation. Instead of the rain forest that mantles the western slope, we found the eastern slope covered mainly with grass, interspersed with scattered trees and clumps of brush, especially along the streams. The lower land in the trough is semiarid. The

---

* See Maps VII and VIIIa, pp. 287 and 288, below.

lower slopes of the Cordillera Occidental, as well as the trough to the east, support a considerable population. In the trough, however, grazing seems to be the principal occupation. The outstanding geological and geographical features along the western border of the trough are indicated by the following notes, which, in the absence of photographs, are tied to Map VII by reference letters.

At *A*, latitude 2°8′ N., the Río Patía follows a contact between bright-red homogeneous rocks west of the river and layered sediments, dipping eastward about 25 degrees, east of it. This contact follows the river for about 15 miles to the north. At *B*, on the divide between the Río Patía and the Río Cauca, we flew over a contact between what appeared to be igneous rocks composing the Cordillera Occidental and sedimentary rocks dipping very steeply to the east. To the east for 15 to 20 miles is a broken, low hilly land underlain by dipping sediments and rising gradually toward the steep front of the Cordillera Central. This region is mainly grassland.

Beginning at *C*, latitude 2°36′ N., the Río Cauca flows immediately east of a belt, half a mile to 2 miles wide, of sharp ridges formed by relatively thin beds of resistant sedimentary or metamorphosed sedimentary rock standing practically vertical. Everywhere south of the point *D*, about 35 miles south of Cali, the bottom of the trough is being eroded. Along its western side the floor is composed of sedimentary rocks dipping in general toward the east and considerably faulted. The Cordillera Occidental appears to be composed of intrusive or metamorphic rocks or both. Toward the south, the bottom of the trough rises gradually and is trenched deeply by tributaries of the Río Patía, forming a rugged region not much lower than the mountains on each side. Around and north of Cali and for several miles to the south, the bottom of the trough is a flat alluvial plain.

At *D*, after crossing to the eastern side of the Río Cauca, we came over a thickly settled region that contrasted strongly with the predominantly pastoral lands farther south along the route. It is a low mature hill land, with the houses on the divides. The farms are small and are largely in grass, with some acreage devoted to cultivated crops and orchards. The natural vegetation in this part of the valley is mainly low brush.

As we approach Cali, at *E*, the population density increases. Most of the people seem to live on individual farms in neat red-brick houses with tile roofs. Aside from the large part of the land devoted to pasture, the crops noted were corn, bananas, and pineapple. Clumps of giant bamboo, much used in this part of Colombia, are common along the streams. Their spreading fernlike leaves make an especially pleasing pattern when seen from above. In Cali, bamboo poles were noted that measured 6 inches in diameter at the base, 63 feet in length, and 3 inches in diameter at the top. Such poles are used extensively for scaffolding in construction work, as well as for many other purposes. They are reported to sell for 90 centavos each (about 50 cents).

Cali to Ibagué

The route, as described, from Cali to the airport in the Bogotá basin, on the summit of the eastern range of the Andes, follows the Cauca trough northward to a point near Armenia, where it turns eastward across the Cordillera Central, over the city of Ibagué and across the Río Magdalena about 9 miles north of Girardot, to Bogotá.[1]

In Colombia the Andes consist of three distinct and formidable ranges, the Cordillera Occidental, the Cordillera Central, and the Cordillera Oriental. Between the western and central ranges is the long, narrow structural trough of the Cauca Valley, and between the central and eastern ranges is the somewhat similar upper Magdalena Valley. The Cauca trough has a total length of about 220 miles, including its southern end, drained by the Río Patía, and an average width of about 20 miles.

A typical view of the Cauca trough is shown in Figure 305, looking northwest from a point about 21 miles north of Cali. The river flows on a flat alluvial plain close to the base of the western range. Streams from that range are building alluvial fans into the valley, but most of them are small, suggesting that the uplift of the range has been fairly recent. This idea is supported by the abruptness of the lower slopes of the range in contrast with the relatively gentle slopes and old-age topography of its higher parts (see also Figure 308), a condition characteristic of the west-

---

[1] In explanation of the fact that the directions given in the descriptions of the photographs do not correspond with the relative positions of the airplane wings visible in some of the pictures, it should be stated that the flight was actually made in the reverse direction — from Bogotá to Cali.

ern range and of the trough all the way from Cali to its northern end. Recent differential land movements are suggested also by the alluviated, swampy condition of the valley and the position of the river close to the western range. All these features indicate that the western side of the Cauca trough is probably a relatively recent fault. The eastern side is, in general, somewhat less abrupt.

Almost all the flatter parts of the valley are devoted to pasture, perhaps because of the frequency of inundation, but that all of it must be so used is amply disproved by plantations of sugar, coffee, and cacao, noted earlier from the railroad in the vicinity of Tuluá and La Paila. On the higher and drier ground, corn seems to be the principal crop.

A detailed view of land utilization along the eastern side of the trough is afforded by Figure 306, looking east from a position about 6 miles north of Buga. In the foreground is fenced pasture, farther back are small fields of various crops, and at the left center is a grove of the giant bamboos already described. Another view a mile farther north [307] brings out additional features of land utilization in relation to topography. In the foreground are large fields of corn, and in the background are the lower slopes of the Cordillera Central. In the center, at the apex of an alluvial fan that covers all the lower half of the picture, is a small village. Such a location is typical of most of the villages in the trough on both its eastern and western sides. Scarcely a fan of adequate size can be found, from one end of the trough to the other, that does not have its village near the apex. Some of the bigger streams, with larger and flatter fans, localize the more important towns such as Buga and Tuluá. It is on the fans, also, that most of the cultivated land is to be found, and the larger part of the more level land of the trough bottom is devoted to cattle raising.

Another general view, Figure 308, looking north-northwest across the valley from a point about 3 miles northeast of Tuluá (53 miles from Cali), shows features such as those already described, including the straight, abrupt front of the Cordillera Occidental with the old-age topography at the higher elevations. In addition, at the right, is a low, hilly region composed of highly disturbed and weakly consolidated sedimentary rocks (Tertiary), which form a dissected terrace in the trough bottom extending northward for at least 60 miles with a width of 10 to 20 miles or more and rising some 200 to 600 feet above the river. Gently sloping surfaces on the top of the terrace, immediately east of this photograph and elsewhere, prove that a broad pediment once covered much of the terrace at a level only slightly above the hilltops shown in the picture. The hills rise abruptly above the valley plain along a line marked by a distinct ridge of harder rock.

On a bit of flatter land part way up the lower slopes of the Cordillera Central a small city, probably Sevilla [311], stands amid steep slopes planted with a tree crop believed to be bananas. However, in view of the fact that elsewhere in this part of Colombia bananas are planted to provide shade for coffee trees, that is probably the case here, for we are in an important coffee-growing region. The plantations can be seen on the steeper slopes in the foreground.

To supplement the air photographs, a few pictures taken from the ground are introduced to portray more adequately the character of the Cauca Valley. Figure 309, taken about 12 miles northeast of Cali, shows the typical appearance of the flat valley-bottom pastures. Similar grazing lands, with some of the thousands of cattle they support, appear in Figure 310, looking southeast from the south edge of La Paila. This picture also shows the abrupt edge of the dissected Tertiary hill-land terrace described in connection with Figure 308. Scattered palms are common in the Cauca Valley, but it is exceptional to find groves such as that shown in Figure 314, a photograph taken about 10 miles above Zarzal along the railroad to Armenia. In extreme height and slenderness they answer the description of the wax palms discovered by Humboldt in 1801 on the Quindío Pass a few miles to the east.[2]

Clouds prevented the taking of satisfactory pictures of the higher parts of the Cordillera Central, but on an automobile trip over the range from Armenia to Ibagué it was noted that in that section the range is composed mainly of mica schists, with prevailingly eastward-dipping schistosity, cut complexly by dark-colored intrusive rocks (probably mostly diorite), except at the eastern side near Ibagué, where a large body of granite was found. Topographically, the range has a relatively straight, steep lower western slope, a less steep upper western slope, and

---

[2] A. de Humboldt: Vues des Cordillères, et monumens des peuples indigènes de l'Amérique, 2 vols., Paris, 1816; reference in Vol. 1, pp. 71–84.

305. The Cauca trough and the eastern front of the Cordillera Occidental, as seen from a point about 21 miles north-northeast of Cali (NW, from 3°43′ N., 76°23′ W.)

306. Land utilization patterns along the eastern side of the Cauca trough about 6 miles northeast of Buga (E, from 3°59′ N., 76°15′ W.)

307. The alluvial-fan position of the town and cultivated land shown in this view about 7 miles northeast of Buga represents a cultural pattern characteristic of the margins of the Cauca trough (E, from 4°0′ N., 76°14′ W.)

308. The Cauca trough, as seen from a point 3 miles northeast of Tuluá (NNW, from 4°6′ N., 76°9′ W.). The low hill lands in the foreground have been developed on weak sedimentary rocks along the eastern margin of the valley

309. A typical pastoral landscape in the Cauca trough about 12 miles north-northeast of Cali

310. A view southeastward from La Paila across the floor of the Cauca trough to the western foothills of the Cordillera Central

311. A small city surrounded by coffee plantations on the lower slopes of the Cordillera Central, as seen from a position about 26 miles southwest of Armenia (E, from ca. 4°16′ N., 75°59′ W.)

312. The great volcano Tolima towering above the crest of the Cordillera Central about 15 miles northwest of Ibagué (N, from 4°27′ N., 75°21′ W.)

313. A landscape characteristic of the eastern slope of the Cordillera Central near the summit (N, from ca. 4°26′ N., 75°30′ W.)

a maturely dissected eastern slope gradually decreasing in elevation eastward [317]. Two ground views typical of the eastern slope are provided
by Figure 313, not far from the crest, and Figure 315, looking westward
over the town of Cajamarca from a point about halfway between the
crest and Ibagué. On the steep slopes behind the town, corn and small

314. An unusual grove of palms about 10 miles east of Zarzal (from ca. 42°22′ N.,
75°55′ W.)

patches of sugar cane are found almost to the top of the range. The
palms near the summit [313] are no doubt the wax palms discovered by
Humboldt in this same pass.

About 15 miles north-northwest of Ibagué, towering high above the
general crest level of the Cordillera Central, stands the great dormant
volcano, Tolima [312].

Ibagué to Bogotá

From a point about 3 miles east of Ibagué, the town at which land travelers between Cali and Bogotá again take the train after having crossed the Cordillera Central from Armenia by automobile, we look southeastward across the Magdalena Valley [316], a wide structural trough between the Cordillera Central and the Cordillera Oriental. In the foreground is a broad fan sloping eastward from the Cordillera Central. It seems to have been built against a dam formed by the group of *en échelon* fault-block hills in the center, for the fan is "perched" above the gradient of the present streams, which cross the hills in deep canyons that they are actively extending headward into the alluvial plain. The chain of hills detaches itself from the eastern base of the Cordillera Central 20 or 30 miles south of the area pictured and extends diagonally northeastward across the Magdalena trough at an angle to the trend of the individual small mountain masses making up the group. In the far background, under the clouds, is the Cordillera Oriental, and nearer, but on the far side of the Río Magdalena, is a remarkably long, narrow branching ridge that will be seen repeatedly in succeeding pictures. The rainfall in this part of the Magdalena Valley is light. The alluvial plains are grass-covered, and the hills are mostly bare.

A view to the north from a point 16 miles east of Ibagué [317] shows clearly the tilted fault-block nature of the Cordillera Central, the entire eastern slope of which is visible from the crest, over the wing tip on the left, to the Magdalena Valley at the right. The range is evidently composed of homogeneous rocks and is maturely dissected. The appearance from the ground of land like that in the left foreground, as regards both relief and vegetation, is illustrated in Figures 313 and 315. Photographs taken in the opposite direction, toward the south, show a range of similar character except for the fact that 2 or 3 miles from its eastern base it is paralleled by a long, relatively straight ridge that merges northward into the *en échelon* series of ridges seen in Figure 316.

The group of ridges shown in Figure 316 broadens into a large mass of low mountains of complex structure as it approaches the Río Magdalena [318]. We are looking south-southeast from a point about 10 miles west of the river, the course of which can be easily followed around the south end of the fault ridge beyond the stream, thence across the picture toward the left nearly to its left border, and then to the right along the base of the narrow ridge in the background. Girardot, the head of steamer navigation on the river, lies under a patch of haze about 2 inches to the left of the point where the river bends around the end of the ridge.

The Río Magdalena flows at an angle across the series of *en échelon* fault ridges already mentioned. In Figure 319 we are looking about S. 25° E. diagonally across the Magdalena trough to the Cordillera Oriental on the sky line. Girardot, covered by a patch of haze, lies beyond the ridge, at the right center, in a broad structural basin traversed by the Río Bogotá, between the nearer large ridge and the more distant long, branching ridge mentioned in connection with Figure 316.

In the lower parts of the Magdalena Valley the natural vegetation consists of brush, as may be seen on the slopes of the nearer hills. Only a small fraction of the land is cultivated.

In Figure 320 we are looking north along the western front of the Cordillera Oriental from a point about 6 miles east of the Magdalena. The mountains in this picture seem to constitute a gigantic foothill terrace in front of the higher range to the east. At the upper left are the Magdalena trough and river.

The western summit of the Cordillera Oriental in this region is an enormous west-facing cuesta [321] formed by the hard Guadalupe sandstone (Upper Cretaceous), about 1000 feet thick, that dips eastward under the broad highland basin in which Bogotá is situated. Below the sandstone lies a great thickness of weak, dark-colored Cretaceous shales forming the slopes below the sandstone cliff. Along the Girardot-Bogotá railway a few miles north of this picture, these slopes support an important coffee industry. Where the natural vegetation does not furnish sufficient shade for the coffee trees, bananas have been planted to serve this purpose.

The Bogotá basin (the Sabana de Bogotá) is a remarkable mountain-rimmed plain [322] standing between 8500 and 9000 feet above the sea on what is essentially the broad crest of the eastern range of the Andes. Having a width of about 20 miles and a length several times as great, an ample rainfall, and a cool, healthful climate, it became one of the prin-

315. A village in the Cordillera Central about 10 miles from the eastern border of the range and 11 miles west of Ibagué

316. A view across the Río Magdalena trough between the Cordillera Central and the Cordillera Oriental (SE, from 4°27′ N., 75°11′ W.)

317. The maturely dissected eastern slope of the Cordillera Central, as seen from a position 15 miles east of Ibagué (N, from 4°28′ N., 75°1′ W.)

318. Low mountains in the Magdalena trough, as seen from a point about 14 miles northwest of Girardot (SSE, from 4°28′ N., 74°55′ W.)

319. The Río Magdalena crossing a series of fault ridges in the Magdalena trough, as seen from a position 13 miles north of Girardot (S, from 4°29′ N., 74°51′ W.)

320. A view along the western side of the Cordillera Oriental from a point about 18 miles northeast of Girardot (N, from 4°31′ N., 74°41′ W.)

321.   A portion of the great sandstone escarpment which forms the western crest of the Cordillera Oriental, as seen
       from a point about 21 miles west-southwest of Bogotá (SE, from 4°33′ N., 74°23′ W.)

322.   The Bogotá basin about 5 miles west of Bogotá (SE, from 4°37′ N., 74°9′ W.)

323. A view across the Bogotá basin from Montserrate on the outskirts of the capital city (WNW)

324. Mountain agriculture on the eastern slopes of the Cordillera Oriental about 13 miles south-southeast of Bogotá on the road to Villavicencio

325. The Salto de Tequendama, where the waters of the Bogotá basin cascade over its western rim 16 miles west-southwest of Bogotá.

cipal centers of settlement in Colombia and the site of the capital city. In this picture we are looking southeast across the plain from a position about 5 miles west of Bogotá.

A better idea of the nature and extent of the Bogotá basin may be gained from Figure 323, taken from the summit of a mountain (Montserrate) that rises abruptly above the eastern border of the city of Bogotá. We are looking west across the basin to the mountains on its western border (the same as those seen from the opposite direction in Figure 321), which here do not rise to great heights above the plain. In the foreground are the northern part of the city and the new site of the university (right of center).

A glimpse of the mountains east of the Bogotá basin is afforded by Figure 324, looking eastward a few miles above Cáqueza on the motor road to Villavicencio, at the edge of the llanos. In spite of a rugged topography, this region is intensively cultivated, corn being the principal crop. Cornfields cover much of the mountain slope at the left and are found in almost every spot where enough soil exists to nourish the crop.

The drainage of the Bogotá basin gathers in the Río Bogotá, which, about 16 miles west of the city, plunges over the edge of the sandstone cliff forming the cuesta of Figure 321 in an exceptionally beautiful waterfall [325], the Salto de Tequendama, where the river makes a sheer leap of about 450 feet. The falls are also shown from the air in the small inset. Without detracting from the beauty of Tequendama, the stream has been harnessed at a smaller cataract above the falls to supply electricity for Bogotá. A drop of about 6000 feet in 15 miles below the falls would seem to offer possibilities for much additional power. Aside from its height and volume, a feature that lends particular charm to Tequendama is a steplike ledge of rock below the brink of the falls that breaks the water into many separate masses, most of which dissolve into spray and mist before they reach the bottom.

Cali to Antioquia

From Bogotá we returned to Cali, whence we flew without stop to Cristobal in the Canal Zone. No pictures were taken on this flight, but I have tried to record in words some of the salient geographic features of this not too well known region. We traced the Río Cauca to a point within 5 or 6 miles of the city of Antioquia, then turned northwestward across the Cordillera Occidental and followed the Río Sucio and the Río León to a point near the head of the Golfo de Urabá. From there we crossed the Isthmus of Panamá to the head of the Golfo de San Miguel and then flew along the south side of the Isthmus to the Canal Zone. Descriptions of the country along this route are keyed to the flight map by letters (Map VIIIa, p. 288, below).

For the first 100 miles, to Cartago, we followed the Cauca trough, which, for the 75 miles between Cali and Zarzal, was pictured and described in connection with the flight from Cali to Bogotá. Nothing more need be said about this part of the route except that at many places, especially in the vicinity of *A* (see also Figure 305), the higher parts of the Cordillera Occidental west of the trough have a strikingly old-age topography and that the preferential location of towns on the upper parts of the alluvial fans is especially conspicuous all along the western side of the trough.

Extending south for about 15 miles from a point 2 or 3 miles southeast of Cartago, a large ridge within the trough (Cuchilla de Santa Bárbara) rises perhaps 1000 feet above the river. East of the ridge, between it and the base of the Cordillera Central more than 20 miles away, is the northward continuation of the dissected hill land mentioned in the description of Figure 308. It slopes gradually westward from the base of the cordillera as a partly dissected pediment, retaining considerable portions of its original smooth surface on the divides between the dissecting streams. This region, sometimes called the plateau of Armenia after the thriving young city of that name located on its upper slopes, supports an important coffee culture.

From Cartago the route followed within 5 miles of the Río Cauca for about 135 miles to the vicinity of Antioquia. About 8 miles north of Cartago, the Río Cauca enters a narrow, gorgelike valley cut in the hills at the north end of the Cauca trough. Structurally, however, the trough appears to continue with interruptions northeastward toward Manizales. At *B*, 15 miles beyond Cartago, we entered a region of mature topography with a relief of several hundred feet, a thickly settled area devoted mainly to the cultivation of coffee and corn on the steep mountain slopes. Trails and roads follow the divides wherever possible, and several good-sized towns are perched precariously on the narrow hilltops. Belalcázar, for example, is on the summit of a narrow ridge about 2500 feet above the Río Cauca only 3 miles away.

For the next 40 miles along the route, to and beyond the attractive village of Ríosucio, situated on a bit of flatter upland some 3000 feet above the Río Cauca, the land west of the river is very rugged, being maturely dissected and having a relief of 2000 to 3000 feet. It is relatively densely populated, and much of it is intensively cultivated, despite the steepness of the slopes. The land is utilized principally for coffee, corn, and pasture.

East of the river, as far north as C, the topography is more open and the relief more moderate. At C the river, after a sharp bend to the west, turns northward into a deep, narrow V-shaped valley, in which, for many miles, it tumbles in a series of rapids between rugged erosional mountains. A railroad to connect Medellín with the cities of the Cauca trough is now being constructed through this gorge.

Near D there are several sharp rock pinnacles, which look like volcanic plugs. From this vicinity a view to the north, northeast, and east shows a remarkably even sky line (reported to be between 8500 and 9800 feet high) stretching without interruption from the Cordillera Occidental, which rises considerably above it, to the Cordillera Central, which, at its north end, in about this latitude, decreases in elevation and merges into the upland under discussion. This, the plateau of Antioquia, is a maturely dissected former peneplain developed on highly disturbed, predominantly crystalline and metamorphic rocks.[3]

On the western side of the Cauca, at E, the summits of the sprawling ridges and spurs are grass-covered, but the slopes, where not cultivated, are partly clothed with brush. All the way along the route, coffee and corn culture is dominant on the higher mountainsides. The lower slopes and the basin in which Antioquia lies, a few miles farther north, appear to be semiarid. The extreme steepness and ruggedness of the cultivated slopes are surprising. In most places only mule or foot trails connect the fields and villages, some of which seem to be almost inaccessible. For

---

[3] See Pierre Denis: Amérique du Sud (Géographie Universelle, Vol. 15), 2 parts, Paris, 1927, Part 2, p. 244.

instance, 8 or 10 miles back along the route from *E* we passed a sizable village, probably Armenia, on the very top of a ridge so narrow that the large and beautiful church rising from its center occupies most of the flat land. Many of the red-tile-roofed dwellings spill over the limits of the narrow summit on the steep slopes that drop 4000 feet in 5 miles to the Río Cauca.

From Cartago to Antioquia we have passed over a perhaps somewhat rougher than typical part of the most important coffee-growing district in Colombia. In spite of the high relief and extremely steep slopes, the region is relatively densely populated. Probably because of its ruggedness, the land is divided into small individual holdings, which perhaps permit more intensive development than could be accomplished under a system of large holdings and plantation culture, such as that practiced, for example, on the flat lands of the Cauca trough. Soil erosion, though noticeable, does not appear to be extremely serious.

Near Antioquia the valley of the Cauca widens out into a large basin, but a few miles farther north the river again enters a narrow gorge.

Antioquia to Cristobal

Passing Antioquia, about 5 miles to our right, we turned north-north-west over a region of rough, sharp, ridge-and-valley topography. In places the only remaining forest is on the crests of the ridges, the slopes being completely cleared and under cultivation. About 4 minutes later we crossed a pass through the Cordillera Occidental leading to Cañas-gordas and the headwaters of the Río Sucio, a tributary of the Río Atrato. This pass, at nearly 7100 feet,[4] is only 5 miles from the Río Cauca, which has an elevation of about 1800 or 1900 feet north of Antioquia. An interesting stream capture will perhaps occur at some future date.

For the first 10 or 15 miles west of the divide, the region at the head of the Río Sucio has a mature dendritic topography, in which the spurs between tributaries increase in height gradually and evenly to the main divides—indicating, I think, that the streams began their original cutting on a steep scarp slope rather than on an uplifted peneplain like the

---

[4] See Map XIV, Division B, and profile of this map accompanying Report of Corps No. 2, Intercontinental Railway Commission, Washington, 1896.

plateau of Antioquia. In the higher parts of this valley, at *F*, the land is mostly in grass and pasture, and the natural vegetation gives the impression that it was never completely forested. The area is sparsely settled, but the population density increases farther downstream.

According to Denis,[5] it was the natural clearings at the head of the Río Sucio and of the next stream to the south that permitted a localized form of settlement to spread to the western slope of the cordillera. One of these islands of settlement occupies the bottom and lower slopes of the valley of the Río Sucio about 30 miles beyond the pass; its center is Dabeiba, a town in the valley bottom with a population of perhaps 500 to 1000 people. Outside these sheltered valleys the west slope has, according to Denis, not been settled.

A few miles below Dabeiba, at *G*, we reached the western front of the cordillera and came over the lower land of the basin of the Río Atrato. We also left behind all traces of the pioneers who came west down the river from Antioquia. At *H* my notes record: "All jungle — no clearings in sight." At *I*, presumably over Pabarandocito, we left the Río Sucio and within 5 minutes were at *J*, over the muddy waters of the Río León, which we followed until it turned northeast to the Golfo de Urabá. After we left the vicinity of Dabeiba, only one indication of human habitation was noted until we reached the vicinity of El Real, on the south side of the Isthmus of Panamá, though undoubtedly there were small native settlements in the forests that escaped observation. The lowland is covered by an unbroken forest, except for a strip 10 or 15 miles wide along the flood plain of the Río Atrato and on its delta where grassy swamps have not yet been invaded by the forest.

The Río Atrato was crossed at *K*, about 8 miles southwest of the head of the Golfo de Urabá, and the course was set about N. 67°W. across the Isthmus of Panamá for the head of the Golfo de San Miguel. About 6 miles beyond the river, at *L*, the elevation of the land had risen and a beautiful vertical waterfall, some 300 to 350 feet high, broke the monotony of the forest about a mile to the right. At *M*, about 19 miles beyond the Río Atrato, we were over the divide on the Isthmus of Panamá. To the northwest it appears as a rather narrow, even-crested ridge for 50 miles or more, but to the left the divide is inconspicuous.

---

[5] Denis, *op. cit.*, Part 2, p. 248.

All is unbroken forest. About 18 miles beyond the divide we passed the first of several small settlements along the Río Tuira, which are apparently engaged in banana culture. Aside from these settlements, no clearings or other signs of human occupation were seen anywhere in Panamá until we were within a few miles of the Canal Zone.

The main highlands of the Isthmus follow close to the north shore. Most of its southern part is a forested lowland, drowned and embayed along the southern coast (Golfo de San Miguel).

A significant structural feature of the eastern part of the Isthmus is a string of short, low ridges, composed of mainly northeast-dipping bedded rocks, arranged *en échelon* along the northern side of the eastern (Río Tuira) extension of the Golfo de San Miguel. They extend from a point north of *N* west-northwest for more than 30 miles to and beyond La Palma. Each ridge strikes northwest, and the ridge to the west of it is offset to the south. This feature, when studied more carefully, may be useful in interpreting the structural history of the Isthmus.

West of the Golfo de San Miguel we found the peninsula at *O* to be a flat plain cut by tidal marshes and channels. Flying a few miles offshore farther west, we could see that the coastal plain is generally flat and swampy and the water offshore very shallow, except that at *P* small, hilly islands project above the shallow sea.

The islands in the Golfo de Panamá—Isla del Rey and the Archipiélago de las Perlas west of it—all show evidence of relatively recent submergence of the region. The islands appear to represent the higher parts of a mature topography of dendritic pattern now mostly submerged. No structural trends are visible from a distance, a fact which suggests that the islands are composed of essentially homogeneous rocks. The coastal region southwest of the city of Panamá appears to have been similarly submerged.

At *Q*, about 15 miles east of Panamá, a series of 20 or more parallel beach ridges borders the shore and extends eastward some 15 miles to the Río Chepo. West of *Q*, however, the coastal plain narrows and ends within a short distance. Inland, low hills, without distinctive pattern, rise gradually toward the center of the Isthmus. As we crossed the Isthmus 5 or 6 miles northeast of the canal, we found a fine-textured topography of moderate relief, cleared here and there along the roads, but elsewhere covered with forest.

At Cristobal the flight around most of the continent of South America was ended, and this paragraph concludes an attempt to convey by means of photographs and word descriptions a more comprehensive and connected impression than could otherwise be had of the lands to the south of us—of their geological constitution, their physical features, and their vegetation, and of the manner and extent of the utilization of these natural features and the human adaptation to them. We have tried to depict the setting in which the drama of life in South America is being played, leaving for others the task of portraying the actors and their works.

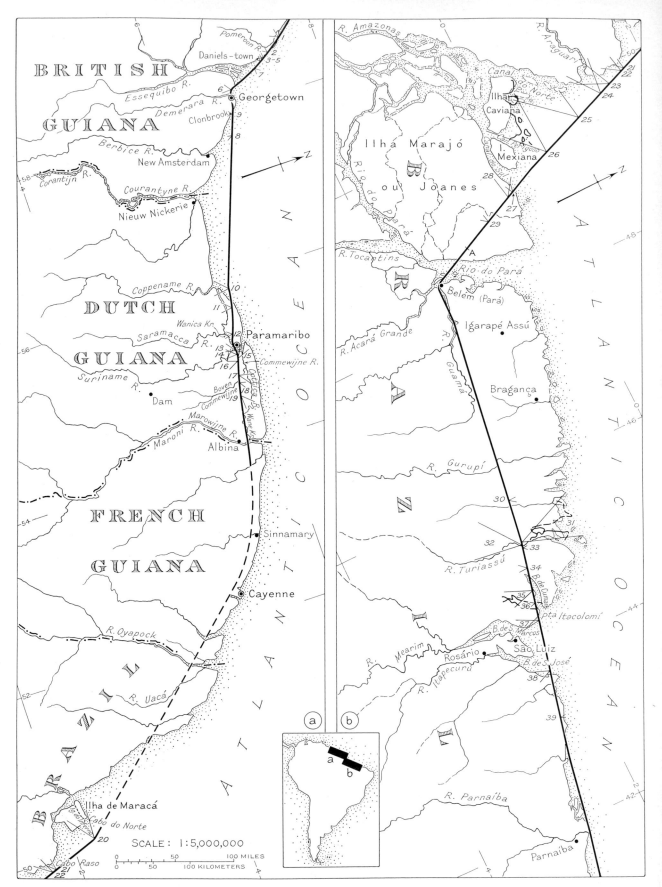

MAP II. Flight route and location, direction, and range of photographs, British Guiana to Parnaíba, Brazil. Broken line indicates that exact flight-line position is uncertain. In the coastal areas covered by Figures 26, 31, and 35, the photographs suggest inaccuracies in the existing maps. The alterations that seem to be indicated are shown with heavy lines. See text references on pages 20, 28, and 29.

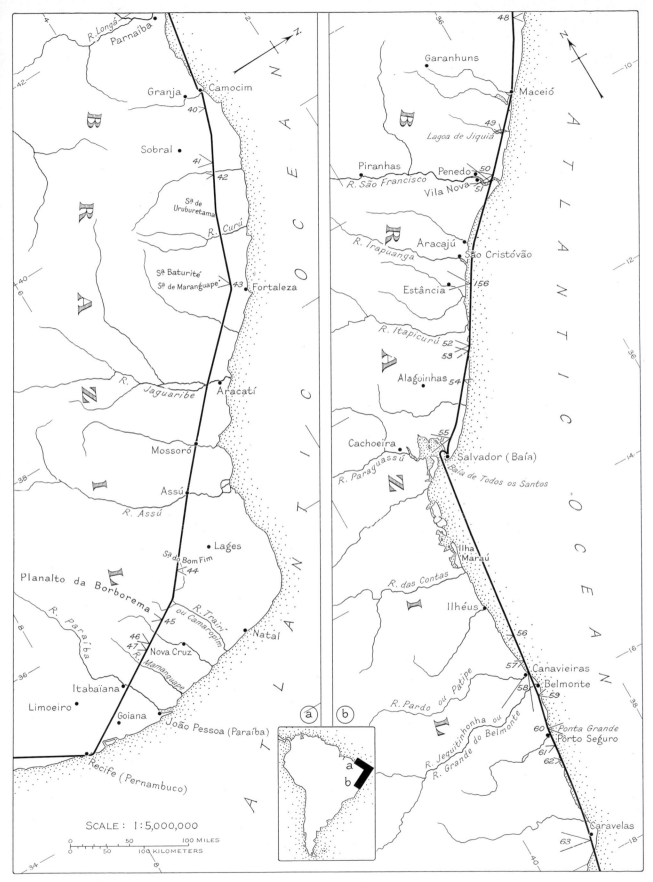

MAP III. Flight route and location, direction, and range of photographs, Parnaíba, Brazil, to Caravelas, Brazil.

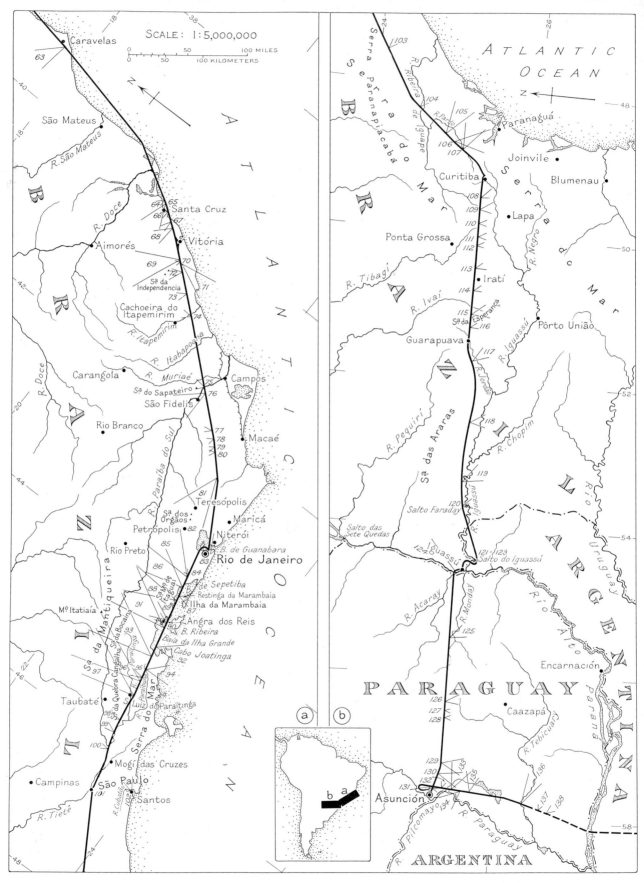

MAP IV. Flight route and location, direction, and range of photographs, Caravelas, Brazil, to southern Paraguay. Broken line indicates that exact flight-line position is uncertain.

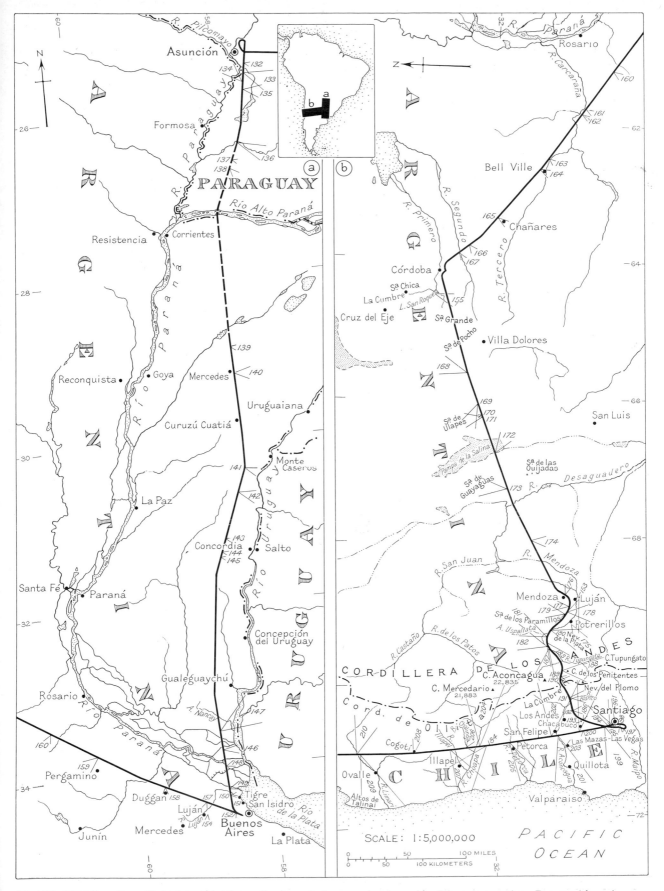

MAP V. Flight route and location, direction, and range of photographs, Asunción, Paraguay, south to Buenos Aires, Argentine Republic, and west to central Chile. Broken line indicates that exact flight-line position is uncertain.

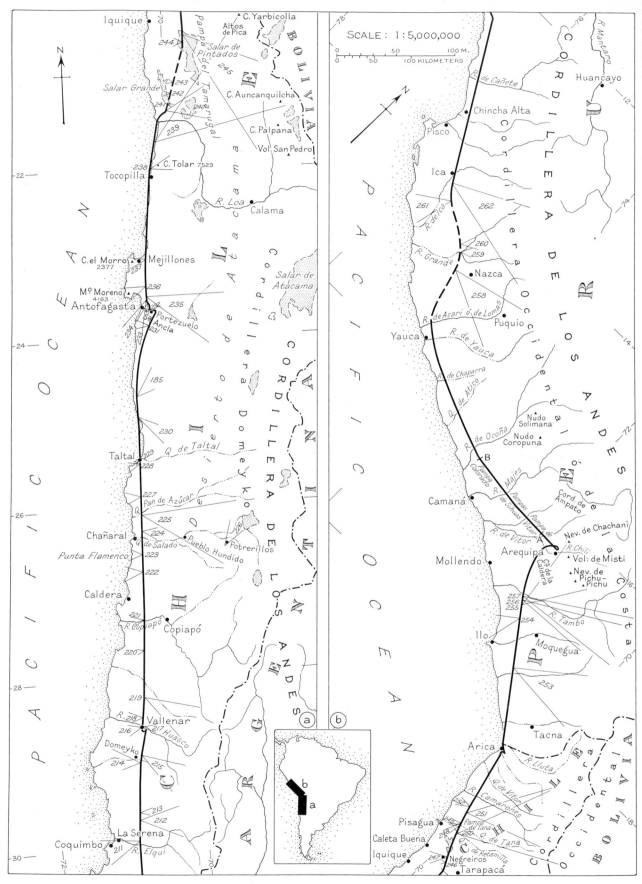

MAP VI. Flight route and location, direction, and range of photographs, from the Río Elqui in central Chile to the Río de Cañete in Peru. Broken line indicates that exact flight-line position is uncertain.

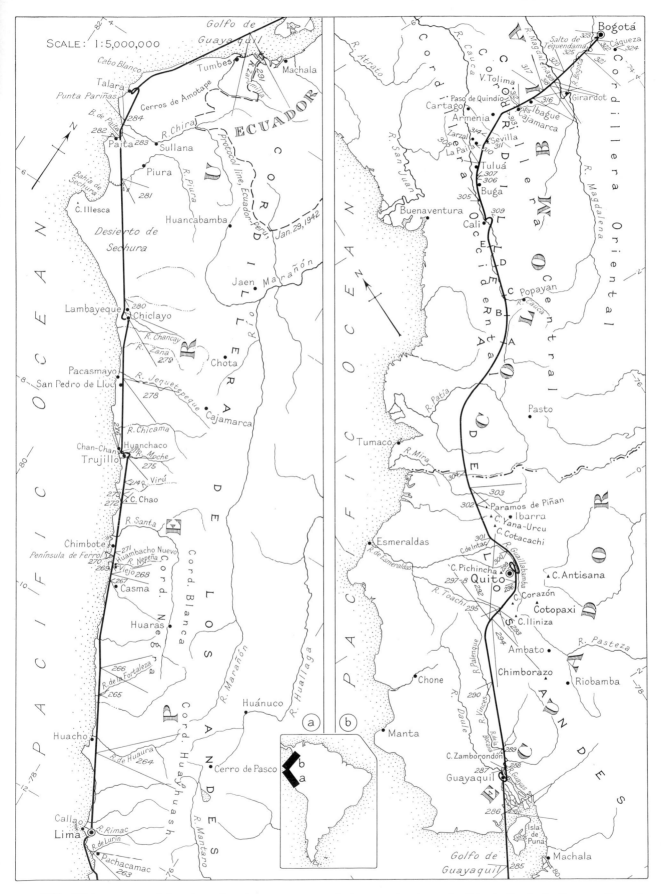

MAP VII. Flight route and location, direction, and range of photographs, from the Río de Lurín in Peru to Bogotá, Colombia.

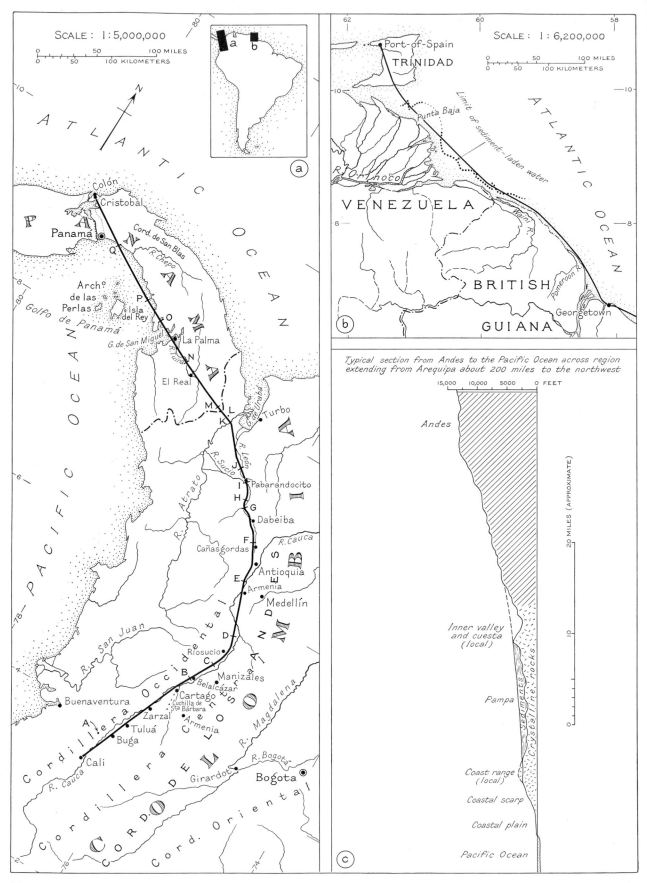

MAP VIII. a. Flight route and points of reference for observations (designated by capital letters), Cali, Colombia, to Cristobal, Canal Zone. b. Flight route from Port-of-Spain, Trinidad, to Georgetown, British Guiana, and the seaward limit of sediment-laden water opposite the main mouths of the Orinoco. c. Typical section from Andes to the Pacific Ocean, southern Peru.

INDEX

Numbers in brackets refer to photographs. Abbreviations: *Arg.*, Argentine Republic; *Col.*, Colombia; *E. Braz.*, Eastern Brazil (Recife to Vitória); *Ecua.*, Ecuador; *Gui.*, Guianas; *NE. Braz.*, Northeastern Brazil (Mouths of the Amazon to Recife); *Pan.*, Panama; *Para.*, Paraguay; *SE. Braz.*, Southeastern Brazil (Vitória to Iguassú Falls); *Venez.*, Venezuela.

AMERICAN GEOGRAPHICAL SOCIETY

Partial List of Publications

"SPECIAL PUBLICATIONS" SERIES

[No. 1]–*Memorial Volume of the Transcontinental Excursion of 1912 of the American Geographical Society of New York*. Edited by W. L. Joerg. 418 pp., 116 maps, diagrams, and photographs. 1915.

[No. 2]–*The Andes of Southern Peru: Geographical Reconnaissance Along the Seventy-Third Meridian*. By Isaiah Bowman. 1916. (Out of print.)

[No. 3]–*The Frontiers of Language and Nationality in Europe*. By Leon Dominion. 393 pp., 67 maps and photographs, 9 map plates in color. 1917. (Out of print.)

No. 4 – *The Face of the Earth as Seen From the Air: A Study in the Application of Airplane Photography to Geography*. By Willis T. Lee. 122 pp., 82 maps and photographs. 1922.

No. 5 – *Desert Trails of Atacama*. By Isaiah Bowman. 1924. (Out of print.)

No. 6 – *China: Land of Famine*. By Walter H. Mallory. 1926. (Out of print.)

No. 7 – *Problems of Polar Research*. Edited by W. L. G. Joerg. 484 pp., 96 maps, diagrams, and photographs. 1928.

No. 8 – *The Geography of the Polar Regions*. By Otto Nordenskjöld and Ludwig Mecking. 366 pp., 135 maps, diagrams, and photographs. 1928.

No. 9 – *The Coral Reef Problem*. By William Morris Davis. 596 pp., 227 maps, diagrams, and photographs. 1928.

No. 10 – *Richard Hakluyt and the English Voyages*. By George Bruner Parks. 306 pp., 32 halftone reproductions. 1928.

No. 11 – *Brief History of Polar Exploration Since the Introduction of Flying*. By W. L. G. Joerg. Accompanying maps of the Arctic and Antarctic on the scale of 1:20,000,000. 1930. (Out of print.)

No. 12 – *Peru from the Air*. By George R. Johnson. 171 pp., 141 aerial photographs. 1930.

No. 13 – *The Pioneer Fringe*. By Isaiah Bowman. 1931. (Out of print.)

No. 14 – *Pioneer Settlement*. Edited by W. L. G. Joerg. 1932. (Out of print.)

No. 15 – *The Grand Coulee*. By J. Harlen Bretz. 99 pp., 38 photographs, 15 line drawings, 1 insert map in color, and 8 stereoscopic views. 1932.

No. 16 – *New England's Prospect: 1933*. Edited by John K. Wright. 509 pp., 9 double-page maps, 26 smaller maps, and 13 diagrams. 1933.

No. 17 – *The Discovery of the Amazon According to the Account of Friar Gaspar de Carvajal and Other Documents*. 483 pp., 1 map and facsimiles of 2 documents. 1934.

No. 18 – *The Fiord Region of East Greenland*. By Louise A. Boyd and others. 381 pp., 2 maps, 361 photographs in text accompanied by slip case with 14 plates. 1935.

No. 19 – *The Colorado Delta*. By Godfrey Sykes. 200 pp., 74 maps and photographs. 1937.

No. 20 – *Polish Countrysides*. By Louise A. Boyd. 247 pp., 9 maps, 486 halftones. 1937.

No. 21 – *Rainfall and Tree Growth in the Great Basin*. By Ernst Antevs. 104 pp., 6 maps and 1 diagram in text, 2 plates. 1938.

No. 22 — *Northernmost Labrador Mapped from the Air*. By Alexander Forbes and others. 275 pp., 12 maps and diagrams, 166 halftones in text accompanied by slip case containing 6 plates and "Navigational Notes on the Labrador Coast," by Alexander Forbes. 1938.

No. 23 — *White Settlers in the Tropics*. By A. Grenfell Price. 325 pp., 30 maps and diagrams, 58 halftones. 1939.

No. 24 — *Environment and Conflict in Europe*. 18 maps in color on a single sheet (35 x 45 inches) with a pamphlet of descriptive text. 1940.

No. 25 — *Focus on Africa*. By Richard Upjohn Light. Photographs by Mary Light. 243 pp., 323 photographs, 14 maps. 1941.

No. 26 — *The Face of South America: An Aerial Traverse*. By John Lyon Rich. 319 pp., 325 photographs, 8 maps. 1942.

OTHER PUBLICATIONS DEALING WITH LATIN AMERICA

Maps

Map of Hispanic America, 1:1,000,000. 101 (of a total of 107) sheets in color, published prior to March 1, 1942.

Map of the Americas, 1:5,000,000. 3 sheets in color covering Latin America and a part of the United States. 1942.

Books and Pamphlets

The Agrarian Indian Communities of Highland Bolivia. By George McCutchen McBride. 27 pp., 5 maps and photographs. *Research Series No. 5*. 1921.

Recent Colonization in Chile. By Mark Jefferson. 52 pp., 15 maps, diagrams, and photographs. *Research Series No. 6*. 1921.

The Rainfall of Chile. By Mark Jefferson. 32 pp., 10 maps and diagrams. *Research Series No. 7*. 1922.

A Catalogue of Geological Maps of South America. By Henry B. Sullivan. 191 pp., 1 map. *Research Series No. 9*. 1922.

Geography of the Central Andes: A Handbook to Accompany the La Paz Sheet of Hispanic America on the Millionth Scale. By Alan G. Ogilvie. 240 pp.; 43 maps, diagrams, and photographs. *Map of Hispanic America Publication No. 1*. 1922.

The Land Systems of Mexico. By George McCutchen McBride. *Research Series No. 12*. 1923. (Out of print.)

Peopling the Argentine Pampa. By Mark Jefferson. 211 pp., 67 maps, diagrams, and photographs, 1 plate. *Research Series No. 16*. 1926.

Catalogue of Maps of Hispanic America. Published by countries, in 4 volumes, containing 1068 pp., 15 maps. *Map of Hispanic America Publication No. 3*. 1930–1933.

Chile: Land and Society. By George McCutchen McBride. 408 pp., 58 maps, facsimiles, and photographs. *Research Series No. 19*. 1936.

The European Possessions in the Caribbean Area. 116 pp.; insert map in 3 colors. *Map of Hispanic America Publication No. 4*. 1941.